STEM mindset™

ADDITION & SUBTRACTION

with **LEGO**® *and* **BRAINERS**™

Grades 1-2 (A)

Ages 6-8

Table of Contents

Common Core State Standards

SKILLS in	Counting, Number & Operations	Algebraic thinking	Geometry	Measure-ment	Data Analy-sis, Statistics, & Probability
Addition	✓	✓	✓	✓	✓
Congruence	✓	✓	✓	✓	✓
Count	✓	✓	✓	✓	✓
Division	✓	✓	✓	✓	✓
Inequalities	✓	✓	✓	✓	✓
Language	✓	✓	✓	✓	✓
Manipulatives	✓	✓	✓	✓	✓
Match	✓	✓	✓	✓	✓
Pattern	✓	✓	✓	✓	✓
Subtraction	✓	✓	✓	✓	✓
Whole Num-bers	✓	✓	✓	✓	✓
Multiplication	✓	✓	✓		✓
Estimate	✓		✓	✓	✓
Regrouping	✓	✓		✓	✓
More than 2 addends	✓		✓		✓

SKILLS in	Counting, Number & Operations	Alge-braic thinking	Geometry	Meas-urement	Data Analysis, Statistics, & Probability
Number line	✓	✓	✓		
Rounding	✓			✓	✓
Odd/Even	✓				
Place Value	✓				

For Teachers, Homeschoolers, and Parents

Addition and Subtraction with LEGO and BRAINERS

makes the foundations for students' success in MATH and Algebra:

- Common Core State Standards
- preparation for standardized tests such as SCAT®, CogAT®, MAP®, etc.
- covers each grade level in great depth to develop reasoning, critical thinking, and problem-solving skills
- procedural fluency
- modeling and building with Lego bricks
- number sense strategies
- step-by-step strategies
- information coding (color-, border-, line coding)
- visualization and play
- creating a foundation in how numbers work
- alive, engaging, and fun explanations with Brainers
- good training for teachers in how to explain math concepts
- favorite children's font
- answers with step-by-step solutions.

Number Sense Strategy problems implemented within Common Core Math Standards are aimed for students to develop and apply logic and mathematical reasoning skills. The math problems evolve in fun and engaging ways to reinforce visual understanding and make foundations for algebraic thinking and computer programming operations' skills.

The students don't even notice how the problems are becoming more difficult or challenging as the easy way of explanations and fun, and engaging activities keep them captivated and occupied, providing extra depth and enrichment in math conceptual understanding.

Visualization and play with LEGO bricks are the most effective instruments to develop conceptual understanding and cognitive domain reasoning for second-graders.

Numerous Number Sense strategies help students become comfortable and confident with math concepts. Addition and subtraction problems are challenging, but they evolve gradually with Brainers' explanations, and thus, help students build and expand their critical thinking and analytical skills, and reasoning.

Using and creating Number Sense Strategies also help students and teachers forget about "disgusting" and "scary" drill sheets. The engaging activities to fill in, write and make columns teach how to grasp math concepts in an easy and fun way, making the foundations for the most important aim in elementary education – understanding and using strategies to visualize how the numbers work.

Number Sense strategies strengthen understanding of addition and subtraction properties and represent different algorithms to grasp the meaning of place value. Colorful, fun, and engaging visual problems make deep connections between symbolic and visual representations of numbers to help students get the concept of counting and reasoning.

Brainers give easy-to-follow explanations and examples. So, you do not need lengthy teaching manuals. Brainers also give excellent teaching tips and insights for teachers.

Addition and Subtraction with LEGO and Brainers Grades 1-2 is excellent training for teachers on how to explain math concepts, attract students to math beauty, and create life-long learners.

The workbook has answers with step-by-step solutions. You don't need to find complicated Answer Keys. We are all teachers and parents with precious little time. So, we made it easier for you to have a whole page of the math workbook with ready solutions and answers.

We are Brainers. Yes, we live in the Brain. Some say we are thoughts, others insist we are ideas. Some demand we are emotions, others argue we are feelings. Some draw us as experience, others draw us as the future. We do not know who we are. We know that we exist in each Brain. We are what you think or feel when you open your eyes (or maybe when you close them,) when you do whatever you are doing, when you are asked to study, read, calculate, draw, write. We are different, and we want to open the mysterious door to the Wonderful, Amazing, Fantastic, Adventurous World of Math with you. Yes, you hear us right! Math is the BEST thing ever. Let's explore it together!

www.stemmindset.com

I'm the center of the brain (at least, I think so). I'm highly positive, adventurous, and open-minded. I'm ready to help or take any risk. I'm an encouraging and unbelievably positive friend.

I'm the Brain's disrespectful, grumpy, bad-tempered, critical Brainer. I get "crazy-mad," impatient with "any problem," or displeased with "any explanation." I'm often quarrelsome and disagreeable with anything new.

I'm "the-smartest-ever-lived," decisive, and loyal to any problem and any Brainer. I'm sharp, and competent in everything. My common sense can explain any problem or calm down any argument between Brainers. I'm "hard-working and extremely ambitious." So, I'm "too brainy."

I'm very occupied with fear of everything, especially new. I'm the terror of any problem, especially word problems. I get panicky and terrified by many pages of the workbook. I'm a "scaredy-cat" according to some critical members of the Brain but encouraged by others.

I'm enthusiastic, excited, and sure about everything in this wonderful world. I'm extremely good-natured and trusting. I'm often engaged in any activity as I'm enterprising, industrious and cheerful. I'm "too energetic and happy" according to some Brainers.

I love to be "left in peace and alone." I would be a dreamer if not for other Brainers and math. Sometimes I'm ready to give up right away or resist anything new..."WHY should I???" I'm persistent in doing nothing.

www.stemmindset.com

1. <u>Compare</u>, using >, <, =.

3 + 7	…	10 – 2	8 – 5	…	4 – 1
4 + 2	…	9 – 2	7 - 2	…	10 – 6
2 + 5	…	10 – 2	8 – 5	…	10 – 7
6 + 3	…	4 + 3	6 – 4	…	5 – 2

"We need to add 3, 4 and 2". <u>What</u> is the total? Hm…

2 + 3 + 4 = …

3 + 4 + 2 = …

4 + 3 + 2 = …

<u>Why</u> are the sums the same? The order is different!?

The order of addends does not affect the total – the sum will be the same.

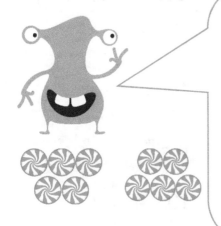

Aha, I remember something about that. I read this summer in an interesting book that this rule is called COMMUTATIVE property.

That's true. 2 candies + 3 candies or 3 candies + 2 candies = always 5 candies!

1.   Number Sense Strategy (NSS). <u>Find</u> the sums, <u>change</u> the addends' order. The first one is done for you.

$2 + 5 + 3 = 10$ $5 + 3 + 2 = 10$ $3 + 2 + 5 = 10$

$1 + 4 + 2 = ...$ $... + ... + ... = ...$ $... + ... + ... = ...$

$5 + 0 + 5 = ...$ $... + ... + ... = ...$ $... + ... + ... = ...$

$4 + 1 + 3 = ...$ $... + ... + ... = ...$ $... + ... + ... = ...$

$6 + 1 + 3 = ...$ $... + ... + ... = ...$ $... + ... + ... = ...$

2. <u>Complete</u> an addition number sentence with tens and ones.

$16 = 10 + 6$ $18 = ... + ...$ $15 = ... + ...$

$10 = ... + ...$ $13 = ... + ...$ $17 = ... + ...$

$29 = ... + ...$ $24 = ... + ...$ $21 = ... + ...$

3. NSS. <u>Fill in</u> the missing numbers to make the comparison true.

$1 + 9$ $=$ $... - 4$ $9 - 4$ $=$ $... - 2$

$3 + 4$ $=$ $10 - ...$ $10 - ...$ $=$ $1 + 3$

$4 + 4$ $=$ $... + 2$ $... - 5$ $=$ $8 - 7$

$5 - 3$ $=$ $... - 7$ $... + 3$ $=$ $10 - 4$

www.stemmindset.com

1. NSS. <u>Take</u> the number of bricks you see in the picture. If you can divide (or put) bricks equally into each of 2 boxes, <u>write</u> the number of bricks you put into one box (2 = 1 + 1; 4 = 2 + 2, etc.). If you cannot divide them equally into 2 boxes (3 = 1 + 1 + 1, 5 = 2 + 2 + 1, etc.), <u>cross out</u> the picture.

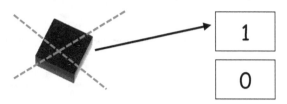

I cannot divide 1 brick equally into 2 boxes, so, I cross it out and write 1 and 0.

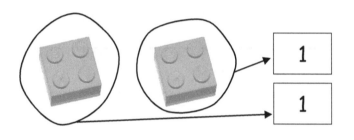

I can put away 2 bricks equally into 2 boxes: 1 + 1, so, I write 1 and 1.

...
...
_____
_____

...
...
_____
_____

1. NSS. <u>Take</u> the number of bricks you see in the picture. If you can divide (or put) bricks equally into each of ⬛2⬛ boxes, <u>write</u> the number of bricks you put into one box (2 = 1 + 1; 4 = 2 + 2, etc.). If you cannot divide them equally into ⬛2⬛ boxes (3 = 1 + 1 + 1, 5 = 2 + 2 + 1, etc.), <u>cross out</u> the picture.

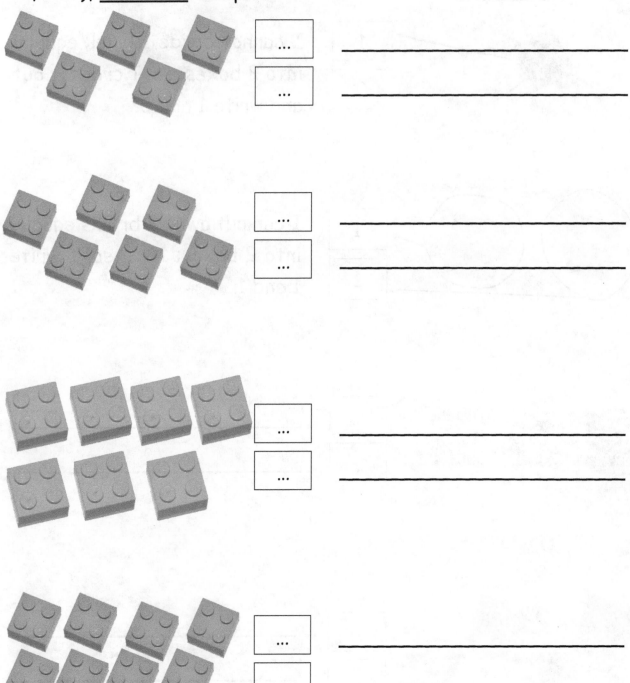

www.stemmindset.com

1.   NSS. <u>Take</u> the number of bricks you see in the picture. If you can divide (or put) bricks equally into each of ⬚2 boxes, <u>write</u> the number of bricks you put into one box (2 = 1 + 1; 4 = 2 + 2, etc.). If you cannot divide them equally into ⬚2 boxes (3 = 1 + 1 + 1, 5 = 2 + 2 + 1, etc.), <u>cross out</u> the picture.

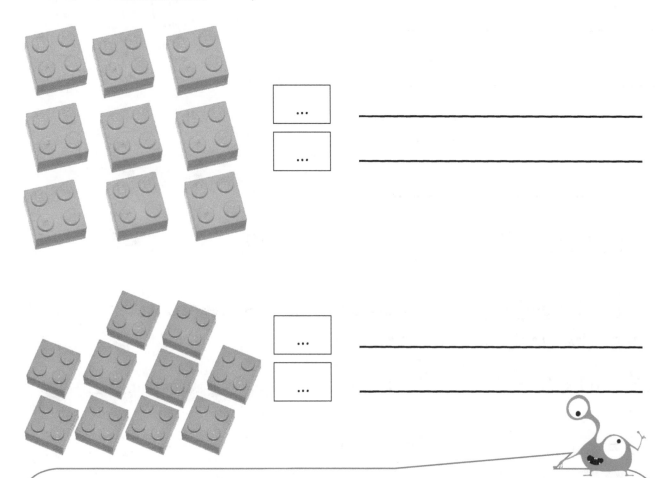

The numbers 1, 3, 5, 7, 9 are indivisible by 2. They always have 1 left over. These numbers are called ODD numbers.

The numbers 0, 2, 4, 6, 8, 10 are divisible by 2. These numbers are called EVEN numbers.

Aha, you hear right. 0 is an even number, too. Just remember this fact. We will learn about zero later, next grade.

1.   NSS. <u>Write</u> 5 number sentences with 3 additions and 3 subtractions so that the value equals 10. The first one is done for you.

6 + 2 - 5 + 9 + 4 – 3 – 3   = 10

_____   = 10

_____   = 10

_____   = 10

_____   = 10

_____   = 10

2. NSS. <u>Complete</u> each addition number sentence with tens and ones. The first one is done for you.

16 = 10 + 6   11 = ... + ...   69 = ... + ...

35 = ... + ...   59 = ... + ...   80 = ... + ...

46 = ... + ...   32 = ... + ...   56 = ... + ...

29 = ... + ...   24 = ... + ...   91 = ... + ...

3. <u>Continue</u> a series of numbers:

5, 10, 15, ..., ..., ..., ..., ..., ...

www.stemmindset.com

1. NSS. <u>Find</u> the difference.

```
    1 4        8 2        4 3        3 1        6 9
  -   4      -   2      -   3      -   1      -   9
  ───────    ───────    ───────    ───────    ───────
    1 0       ...  ...    ...  ...    ...  ...    ...  ...


    1 9        6 7        7 8        9 5        2 9
  -   2      -   5      -   4      -   3      -   8
  ───────    ───────    ───────    ───────    ───────
   ...  ...    ...  ...    ...  ...    ...  ...    ...  ...


    2 5        7 1        6 8        9 2        4 7
  - 1 0      - 3 0      - 3 0      - 5 0      - 1 0
  ───────    ───────    ───────    ───────    ───────
   ...  ...    ...  ...    ...  ...    ...  ...    ...  ...
```

2. <u>Continue</u> a series of numbers:

1, 4, 3, 6, 5, ___, ___, ___, ___, ___, ___, ___, ___.

3. NSS. <u>Complete</u> each addition number sentence with tens and ones. The first one is done for you.

24 = 20 + 4   35 = ... + ...   82 = ... + ...

14 = ... + ...   97 = ... + ...   51 = ... + ...

47 = ... + ...   62 = ... + ...   35 = ... + ...

73 = ... + ...   45 = ... + ...   78 = ... + ...

NSS. <u>Write</u> addition number sentences for each picture. <u>Find</u> the value. <u>Draw</u> the white dots for the addend 1 and the black dots for the addend 2 in the box. <u>Make</u> ten with the biggest number ☺.

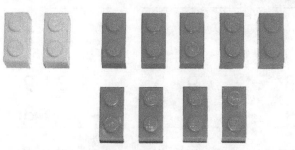

Addend 1   Addend 2

2 + 9 = 9 + 2 = …

Guys, I want to solve it with bricks. I take 2 yellow bricks and 9 red bricks. I prefer to put them in 5's, I like to count by 5's: 5, 10, 15, 20… It's easy. See? I like this math.

Now, I see that 9 is 5 + 4 and 1 red brick is missing. I add 1 yellow brick to make it 10: 9 + 1 = 10. 1 yellow is left: 10 + 1 = 11. I am GENIUS!

I like dots more. First, I draw 2 white dots for yellow bricks and then, add black dots for 9 red bricks. It's fun!

It's much easier to count by 5 and I count dots by 5, too. I add dots: 2 + 3 + 5 = 10 and 1 is left: 10 + 1 = 11.

2 + 9 = 9 + 2 = …

1   1   1   1

I count by 10's. If I have 9, I need 1 more up to 10. I distribute 2 into 1+1. So, 9 + 1 + 1 = 11.

          www.stemmindset.com

NSS. <u>Write</u> addition number sentences for each picture. <u>Find</u> the value. <u>Draw</u> the white dots for the addend 1 and the black dots for the addend 2 in the box. <u>Make</u> ten with the biggest number ☺.

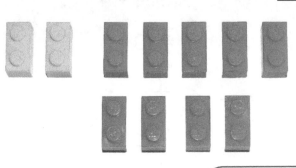

$2 + 9 = 9 + 2 = ...$

$2 + 9 = 9 + 2 = ...$

1   1   1   1

I like numbers, too, don't I? I'm an imagination-abstraction-obsessed Brainer! And I count by 10's!

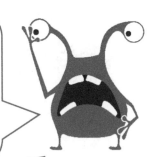

I find out the bigger number – it's 9. If I have 9, I need 1 more to make 10. I take 1 more out of 2. So, 2 = 1 + 1. And 1 + 1 + 9 = 11. Smart? Very smart! By the way, I can also write it as 9 + 1 + 1 = 11. It's up to you. What's easier for you is better.

1. NSS. <u>Complete</u> each addition number sentence with tens and ones. The first one is done for you.

$16 = 10 + 6$ $11 = ... + ...$ $19 = ... + ...$

$13 = ... + ...$ $18 = ... + ...$ $20 = ... + ...$

$23 = ... + ...$ $25 = ... + ...$ $28 = ... + ...$

$27 = ... + ...$ $29 = ... + ...$ $24 = ... + ...$

1. NSS. <u>Find</u> the sum or difference. <u>Read</u> first <u>what</u> your Brainers say☺.

400 + 6 = …   650 + 5 = …   304 + 4 = …

263 + 2 = …   900 + 9 = …   730 + 8 = …

408 – 5 = …   268 – 7 = …   109 – 5 = …

828 – 4 = …   738 – 7 = …   246 – 4 = …

I know how to solve it! We add the digits from the right, right? See, I will be the poet!

Stop talking nonsense! You have something to say – say it!

Sure, sure. We add from the right ones + ones, tens + tens, hundreds + hundreds. We add or subtract only ones in these equations. And we leave the rest of the numbers untouched.

| 400 + 6 = … | → | You add 0 + 6 | → | = 406 |

Let's see. If I want to subtract, I always subtract from the end: ones out of ones, tens out of tens, hundreds out of hundreds. And we leave the rest of the numbers.

| 408 - 5 = … | → | You subtract 5 out of 8 | → | = 403 |

          www.stemmindset.com

1.   NSS. <u>Write</u> addition number sentences for each picture. <u>Find</u> the value. <u>Draw</u> the white dots for the addend 1 and the black dots for the addend 2 in the box. <u>Make</u> ten with the biggest number ☺.

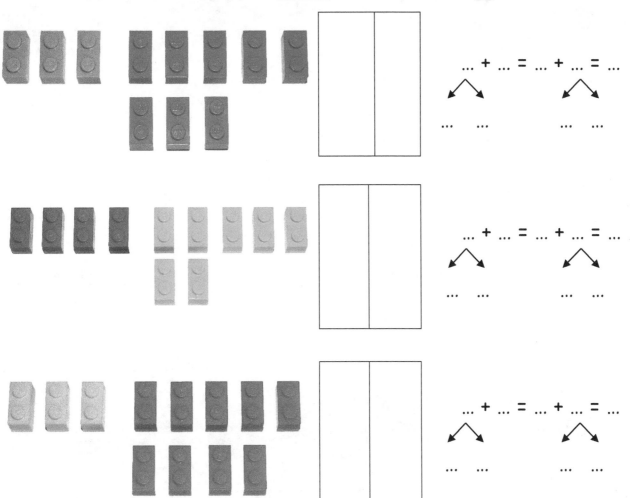

... + ... = ... + ... = ...

... ...

... + ... = ... + ... = ...

... ...

... + ... = ... + ... = ...

... ...

2.   NSS. <u>Find</u> the difference or the sum.

880 – 260 = ...   490 – 170 = ...   380 – 150 = ...

970 – 530 = ...   650 – 240 = ...   760 – 640 = ...

200 + 150 = ...   500 + 370 = ...   800 + 120 = ...

1. NSS. <u>Write</u> all addition or subtraction number sentences with 1, 2, 3, 4, 5, 6, 7, 8, 9, 10, 11, 12, 13, 14, 15, 16, 17, 18, 19, or 20 so the sum or difference equals 13. You can <u>use</u> each number several times.

5 + 8 = 13   ... + ... = ...

... + ... = ... + ... = ...

... + ... = ... - ... = ...

... - ... = ... - ... = ...

... - ... = ... - ... = ...

... - ... = ... + ... = ...

... - ... = ...

2. <u>Write</u> all 2-digit numbers where the tens are 3 more than the ones: _____

_____.

www.stemmindset.com

1. NSS. <u>Take</u> the number of bricks you see in the picture. If you can divide (or put) bricks equally into each of 2 boxes, <u>write</u> the number of bricks you put into one box (12 = 6 + 6; 14 = 7 + 7, etc.). If you cannot divide them equally into 2 boxes (11 = 5 + 5 + 1, 13 = 6 + 6 + 1, etc.), <u>cross out</u> the picture.

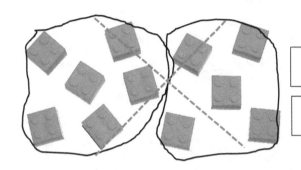

| 6 |
| 5 |

I cannot put away 11 bricks equally into 2 boxes, so, I cross it out and write 6 and 5.

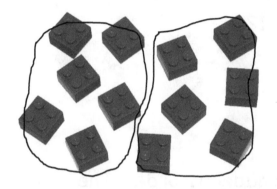

| 6 |
| 6 |

I can put away 12 bricks equally into 2 boxes: 6 + 6, so, I write 6 and 6.

| ... |
| ... |

_____
_____.

| ... |
| ... |

_____
_____

1.   NSS. <u>Write</u> 5 number sentences with 3 or more numbers so that the sum equals 12. The first one is done for you.

4 + 3 + 3 + 2   = 12

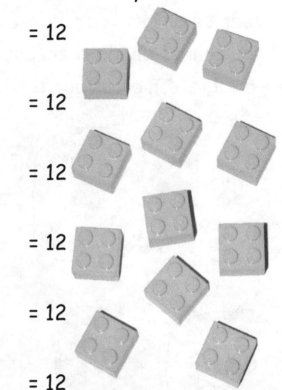

_____   = 12

_____   = 12

_____   = 12

_____   = 12

_____   = 12

2.   NSS. <u>Find</u> the sums and <u>change</u> the addends' order. The first one is done for you.

2 + 5 + 3 = 10	5 + 3 + 2 = 10	3 + 2 + 5 = 10
4 + 3 + 4 = …	… + … + … = …	… + … + … = …
5 + 2 + 3 = …	… + … + … = …	… + … + … = …
6 + 2 + 3 = …	… + … + … = …	… + … + … = …
5 + 4 + 1 = …	… + … + … = …	… + … + … = …

                      www.stemmindset.com

1. NSS. <u>Take</u> the number of bricks you see in the picture. If you can divide (or put) bricks equally into each of ⊡ boxes, <u>write</u> the number of bricks you put into one box (12 = 6 + 6; 14 = 7 + 7, etc.). If you cannot divide them equally into ⊡ boxes (11 = 5 + 5 + 1, 13 = 6 + 6 + 1, etc.), <u>cross out</u> the picture.

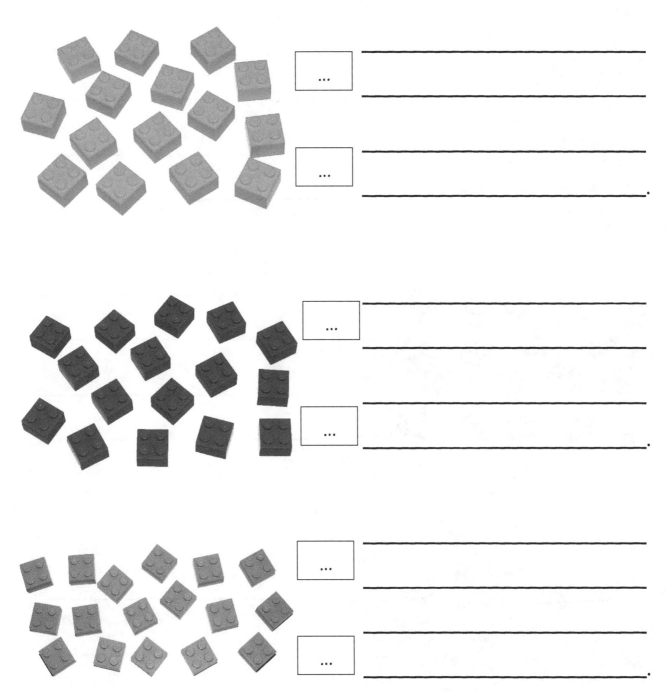

1. NSS. <u>Take</u> the number of bricks you see in the picture. If you can divide (or put) bricks equally into each of ☐2 boxes, <u>write</u> the number of bricks you put into one box (12 = 6 + 6; 14 = 7 + 7, etc.). If you cannot divide them equally into ☐2 boxes (11 = 5 + 5 + 1, 13 = 6 + 6 + 1, etc.), <u>cross out</u> the picture.

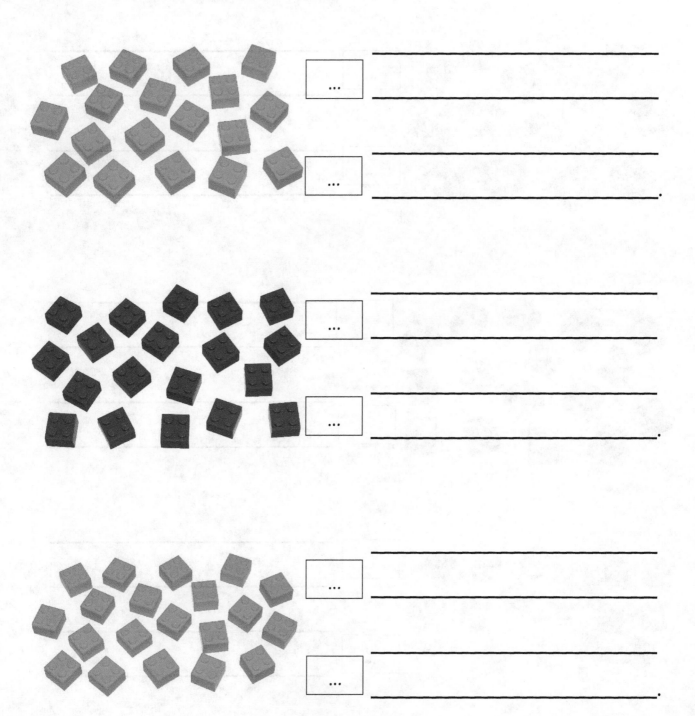

© 2018 STEM mindset, LLC   www.stemmindset.com

The numbers 11, 13, 15, 17, 19 are indivisible by 2. They always have 1 in the remainder (the number that is left over.) These numbers are called ODD numbers.

The numbers 12, 14, 16, 18, 20 are divisible by 2. These numbers are called EVEN numbers.

1. NSS. <u>Find</u> the difference.

```
   3 5        7 2        5 4        6 8        8 7
-    5     -    2     -    4     -    8     -    7
   3 0       … …        … …        … …        … …


   3 5        7 7        6 4        8 2        4 9
-    4     -    2     -    3     -    1     -    5
   … …        … …        … …        … …        … …


   6 5        9 3        5 7        3 9        8 1
-  4 0     -  2 0     -  1 0     -  2 0     -  7 0
   … …        … …        … …        … …        … …
```

2. <u>Cross out</u> the bee which is different.

1. NSS. <u>Write</u> addition number sentences for each picture. <u>Find</u> the value. <u>Draw</u> the white dots for the addend 1 and the black dots for the addend 2 in the box. <u>Make</u> ten with the biggest number ☺.

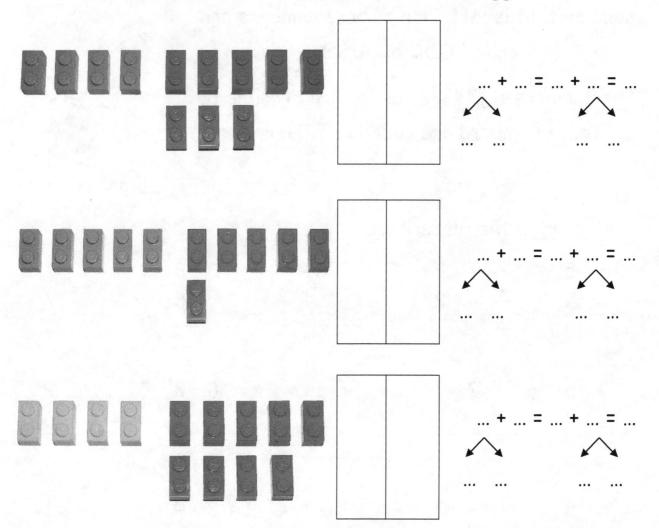

2. The sum of 2 2-digit numbers is 50. Their difference is 30. <u>What</u> are these 2-digit numbers?

Answer: ... ... and ... .

... ... + ... = ... - ... ... = ...

          www.stemmindset.com

1. NSS. <u>Write</u> subtraction number sentences for each picture. <u>Circle</u> the bricks by $\boxed{5's}$. <u>Find</u> the value. <u>Draw</u> the black dots for the minuend and then <u>change</u> the black dots into the white dots to show the subtrahend in the box. <u>Cross out</u> how many bricks you subtract.

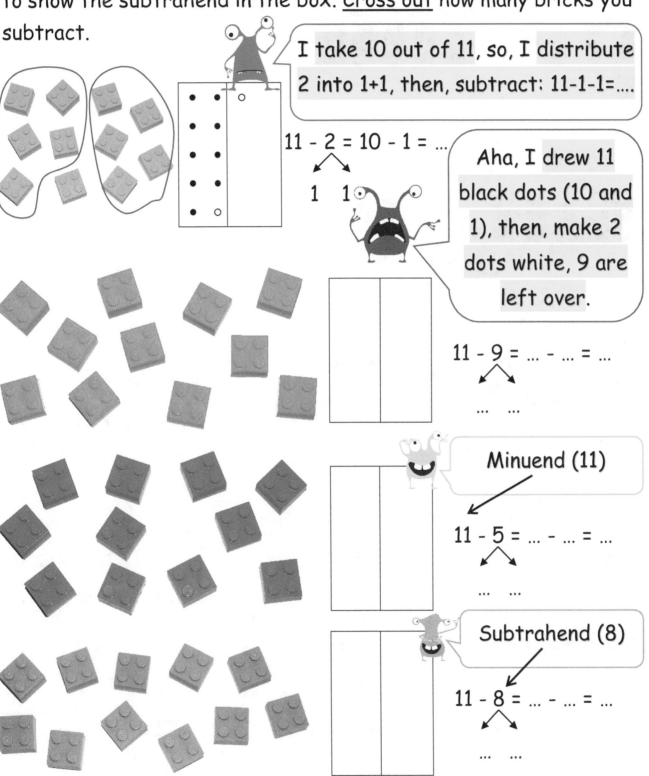

I take 10 out of 11, so, I distribute 2 into 1+1, then, subtract: 11-1-1=....

11 - 2 = 10 - 1 = ...

1   1

Aha, I drew 11 black dots (10 and 1), then, make 2 dots white, 9 are left over.

11 - 9 = ... - ... = ...

...   ...

Minuend (11)

11 - 5 = ... - ... = ...

...   ...

Subtrahend (8)

11 - 8 = ... - ... = ...

...   ...

1. NSS. <u>Write</u> addition number sentences for each picture. <u>Find</u> the value. <u>Draw</u> the white dots for the addend 1 and the black dots for the addend 2 in the box. <u>Make</u> ten with the biggest number ☺.

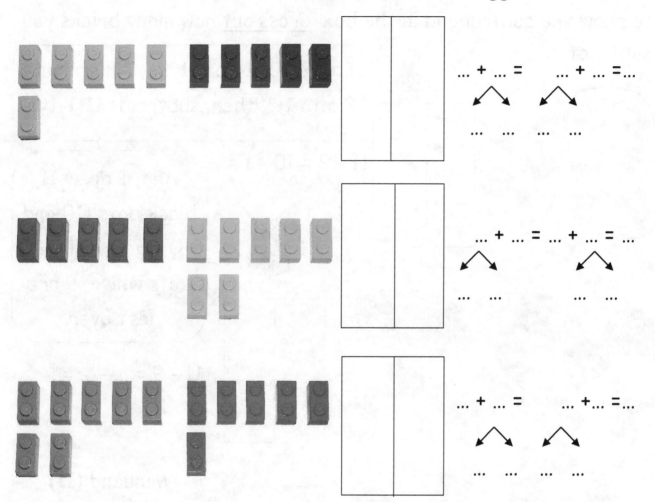

2. NSS. <u>Find</u> the sums.

200 + 300 = ...	400 + 600 = ...	500 + 500 = ...
100 + 600 = ...	200 + 700 = ...	400 + 300 = ...
500 + 400 = ...	800 + 200 = ...	300 + 300 = ...
400 + 400 = ...	200 + 600 = ...	100 + 900 = ...
200 + 500 = ...	400 + 200 = ...	500 + 400 = ...

1.   NSS. <u>Fill in</u> the missing numbers to complete each number sentence. <u>Use</u> the bricks. <u>Circle</u> the bricks to show the difference. You can <u>subtract</u> the leftover bricks in any order and quantity.

11 – 7 = 4

> I circle 4 bricks, 7 are left over. I can arrange them in many ways: 3+4, 2+5, 1+2+3+1.

11 - ... - ... = 4   11 - ... - ... = 4

11 - ... - ... = 4   11 - ... - ... = 4

11 - ... - ... - ... = 4   11 - ... - ... - ... = 4

11 - ... - ... - ... = 4   11 - ... - ... - ... - ... = 4

11 - ... - ... - ... - ... = 4   11 - ... - ... - ... - ... - ... = 4

2.   NSS. <u>Complete</u> each number sentence.

> First, I always look to make 10's.

3 + 4 + 4 = ...   8 + 1 + 3 = ...   5 + 3 + 6 = ...

2 + 6 + 8 = ...   1 + 1 + 9 = ...   4 + 4 + 4 = ...

5 + 3 + 5 = ...   7 + 2 + 7 = ...   6 + 2 + 7 = ...

2 + 9 + 1 = ...   4 + 6 + 3 = ...   7 + 2 + 2 = ...

1.　NSS. <u>Fill in</u> the missing numbers to complete each number sentence. <u>Use</u> the bricks. <u>Circle</u> the bricks to show the difference. You can <u>subtract</u> the leftover bricks in any order and quantity.

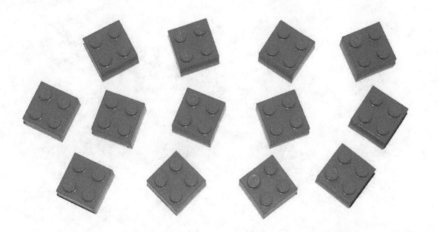

13 – 4 = 7

13 - … - … = 7

13 - … - … = 7

13 - … - … - … = 7

13 - … - … - … = 7

2.　<u>Write</u> 4 number sentences with 3 additions and 3 subtractions so that the value equals 14. The first one is done for you.

4 + 5 - 3 + 7 + 6 – 2 – 3　　　= 14

_____　= 14

_____　= 14

_____　= 14

_____　= 14

 　　www.stemmindset.com

1. NSS. <u>Write</u> subtraction number sentences for each picture. <u>Circle</u> the bricks by 5's. <u>Find</u> the value. <u>Draw</u> the black dots for the minuend and then <u>change</u> the black dots into the white dots (or cross out the black dots) to show the subtrahend in the box.

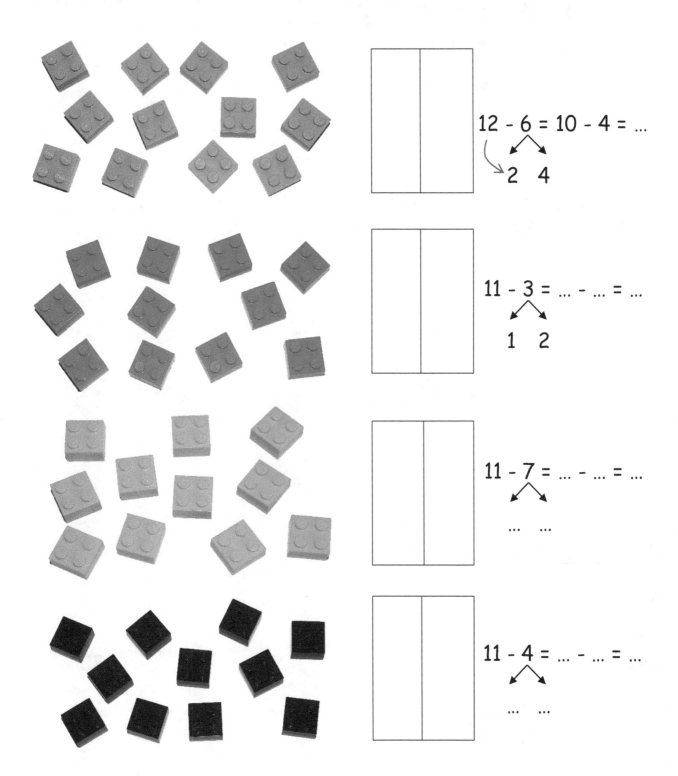

12 - 6 = 10 - 4 = ...
        2 4

11 - 3 = ... - ... = ...
        1   2

11 - 7 = ... - ... = ...
        ... ...

11 - 4 = ... - ... = ...
        ... ...

1.   NSS. <u>Write</u> addition number sentences for each picture. <u>Find</u> the value. <u>Draw</u> the white dots for the addend 1 and the black dots for the addend 2 in the box. <u>Make</u> ten with the biggest number ☺.

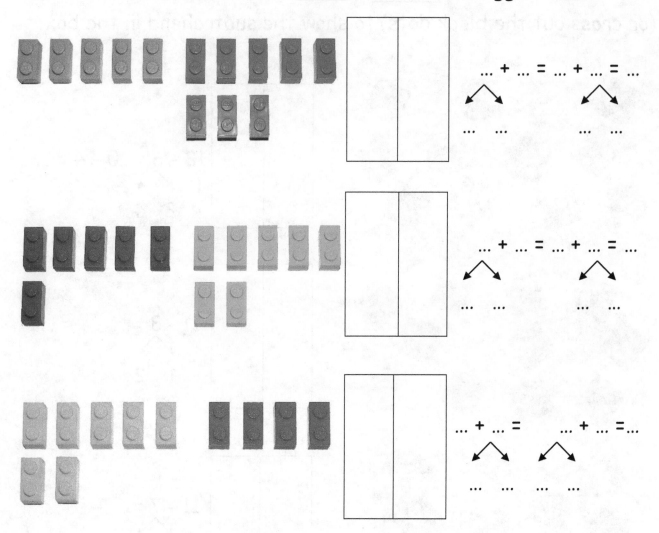

2.   <u>Write</u> the numbers between:

355	...	...	358	638	...	...	641
746	...	...	749	253	...	...	256
962	...	...	965	789	...	...	792

www.stemmindset.com

1. NSS. <u>Write</u> subtraction number sentences for each picture. <u>Circle</u> the bricks by 5's. <u>Find</u> the value. <u>Draw</u> the black dots for the minuend and then <u>change</u> the black dots into the white dots (or cross out the black dots) to show the subtrahend in the box.

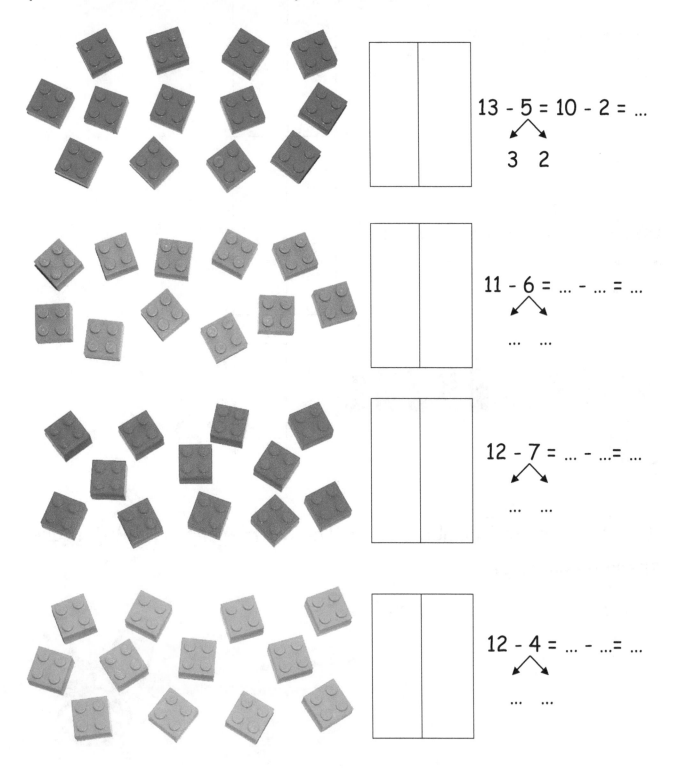

$13 - 5 = 10 - 2 = ...$

3   2

$11 - 6 = ... - ... = ...$

...   ...

$12 - 7 = ... - ... = ...$

...   ...

$12 - 4 = ... - ... = ...$

...   ...

1. NSS. <u>Write</u> addition number sentences for each picture. <u>Find</u> the value. <u>Draw</u> the white dots for the addend 1 and the black dots for the addend 2 in the box. <u>Make</u> ten with the biggest number ☺.

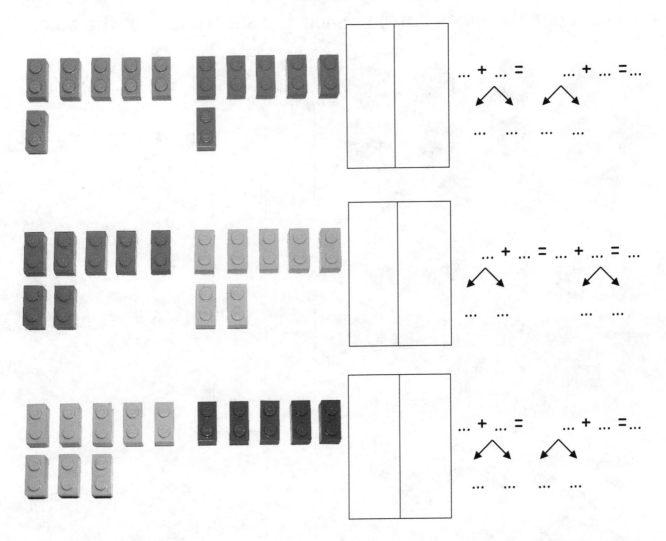

2. The sum of ② numbers is ⑲. Their difference is ③. <u>What</u> are these 2 numbers?

Answer: ... and ....

... + ... = ... - ... = ...

www.stemmindset.com

1.   Continue a series of numbers.

2, 4, 7, 11, _____, _____, _____, _____, _____, _____

1, 6, 9, 14, 17, _____, _____, _____, _____, _____, _____

2.   Fill in the signs "+" or "-" to make the number sentences true.

9 ... 7 ... 5 = 21   9 ... 7 ... 5 = 7

7 ... 5 ... 9 = 11   5 ... 9 ... 7 = 7

3. NSS. Write addition or subtraction number sentences with $\boxed{1,}$ $\boxed{2, 3, 4, 5, 6, 7, 8, 9, 10, 11, 12, 13, 14, 15, 17, 18, \text{or } 20}$ so the sum or the difference equals $\boxed{16}$. You can use each number several times.

7 + 9 = 16   ... + ... = 16

... + ... = 16   ... + ... = 16

... + ... = 16   ... + ... = 16

... - ... = 16   ... - ... = 16

... - ... = 16   ... + ... = 16

... - ... = 16   ... + ... = 16

1.   NSS. <u>Fill in</u> the missing numbers to complete each number sentence. <u>Use</u> the bricks. <u>Circle</u> the bricks to show the difference. You can <u>subtract</u> the leftover bricks in any order and quantity. The first one is done for you.

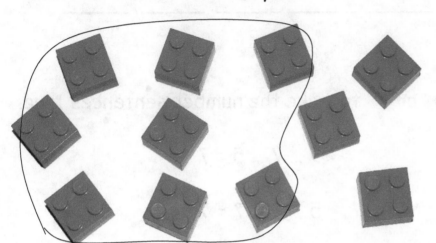

Difference

11 – 3 = 8

11 - 1 - 2 = 8

11 - ... - ... = 8

11 - ... - ... - ... = 8

2.   NSS. <u>Find</u> the value. <u>Do you notice</u> something interesting or weird about these problems?

11 – 5 + 6 = ... 11 – 6 + 5 = ...	14 – 7 + 6 = ... 14 – 6 + 7 = ...
15 – 5 + 6 = ... 15 – 6 + 5 = ...	13 – 5 + 6 = ... 13 – 6 + 5 = ...

I've noticed that _____

_____

_____.

1.   There are ⬚10⬚ bricks of each color. ⬚Make⬚ as many number sentences with the sets of tens (10, 20, 30, 40, etc.).

90 - 20 = 70   90 - … = …   … - … = …

80 - … = …   80 - … = …   … - … = …

40 - … = …   40 - … = …   … - … = …

60 - … = …   60 - … = …   … - … = …

30 - … = …   30 - … = …   … - … = …

20 - … = …   50 - … = …   … - … = …

70 -…=…   70 - … = …   … - … = …

… + … = …   … + … = …   … + … = …

… + … = …   … + … = …   … + … = …

… + … = …   … + … = …   … + … = …

… + … = …   … + … = …   … + … = …

… + … = …   … + … = …   … + … = …

… + … = …   … + … = …   … + … = …

1.　Write ⟦5⟧ number sentences with ⟦3⟧ additions and ⟦3⟧ subtractions so that the value equals ⟦16⟧. The first one is done for you.

2 + 7 - 4 + 8 + 7 – 1 – 3　　　　　= 16

_____　= 16

_____　= 16

_____　= 16

_____　= 16

_____　= 16

2.　NSS. Fill in the missing numbers to complete each number sentence. Use the bricks. Circle the bricks to show the difference. You can subtract the leftover bricks in any order and quantity. The first one is done for you.

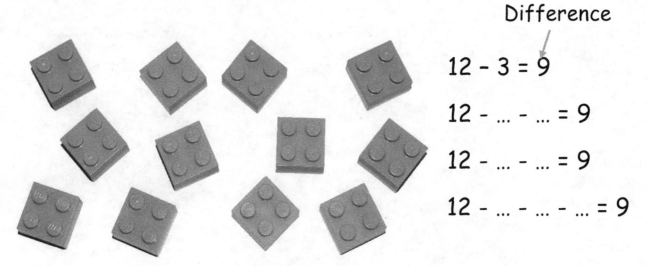

Difference

12 – 3 = 9

12 - … - … = 9

12 - … - … = 9

12 - … - … - … = 9

 　　www.stemmindset.com

1.   NSS. <u>Fill in</u> the missing numbers to complete each number sentence. <u>Use</u> the bricks. <u>Circle</u> the bricks to show the difference. You can <u>subtract</u> the leftover bricks in any order and quantity. The first one is done for you.

12 – 4 = 8

12 - ... - ... = 8

12 - ... - ... = 8

12 - ... - ... - ... = 8

12 - ... - ... - ... = 8

2.   NSS. <u>Write</u> ⑤ number sentences with ③ or more numbers so that the sum equals ⑮. The first one is done for you.

1 + 4 + 6 + 4   = 15

_____   = 15

_____   = 15

_____   = 15

_____   = 15

_____   = 15

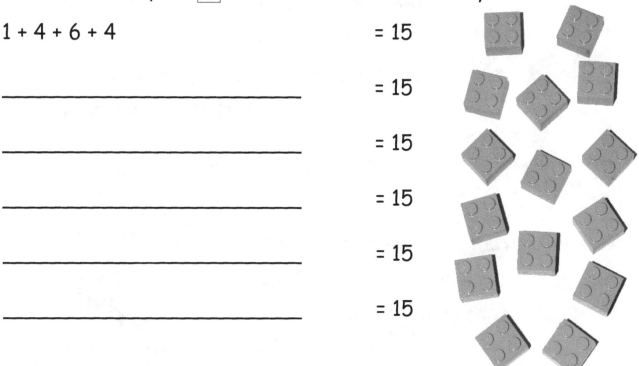

1. <u>Draw</u> an arrow to connect each number sentence with its matching answer on the number line. The first one is done for you.

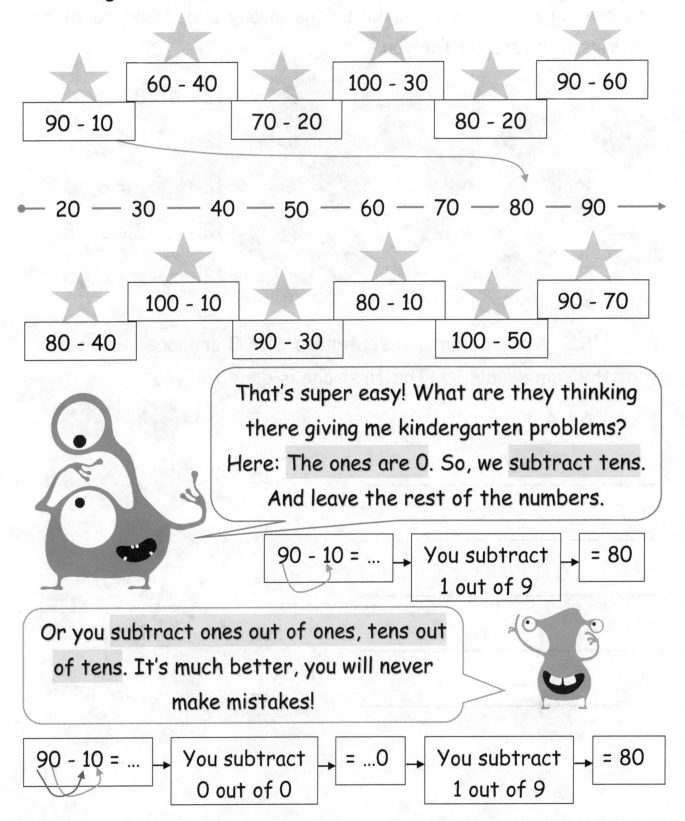

That's super easy! What are they thinking there giving me kindergarten problems? Here: The ones are 0. So, we subtract tens. And leave the rest of the numbers.

Or you subtract ones out of ones, tens out of tens. It's much better, you will never make mistakes!

1. NSS. Write addition number sentences for each picture. Find the value. Draw the white dots for the addend 1 and the black dots for the addend 2 in the box. Make 10 with the biggest number 😉.

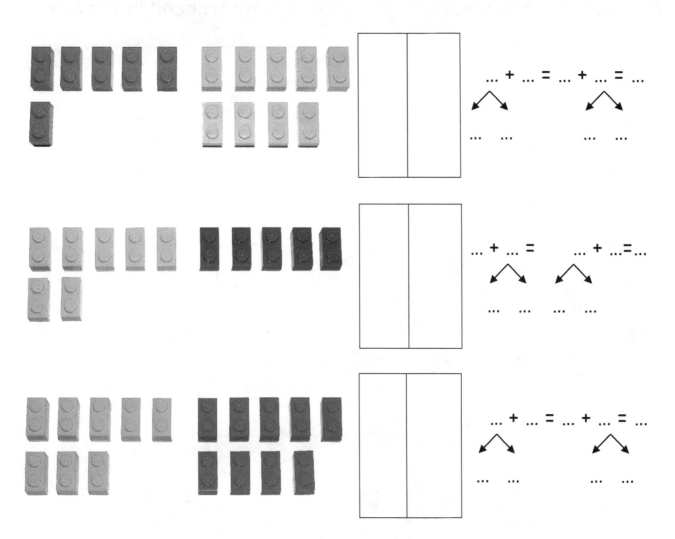

2. Answer the questions.

9361:

The sum of the thousands and ones is _____.

The difference between the tens and hundreds is

_____.

1. NSS. <u>Write</u> subtraction number sentences for each picture. <u>Circle</u> the bricks by 5's. <u>Find</u> the value. <u>Draw</u> the black dots for the minuend and then <u>change</u> the black dots into the white dots (or cross out the black dots) to show the subtrahend in the box.

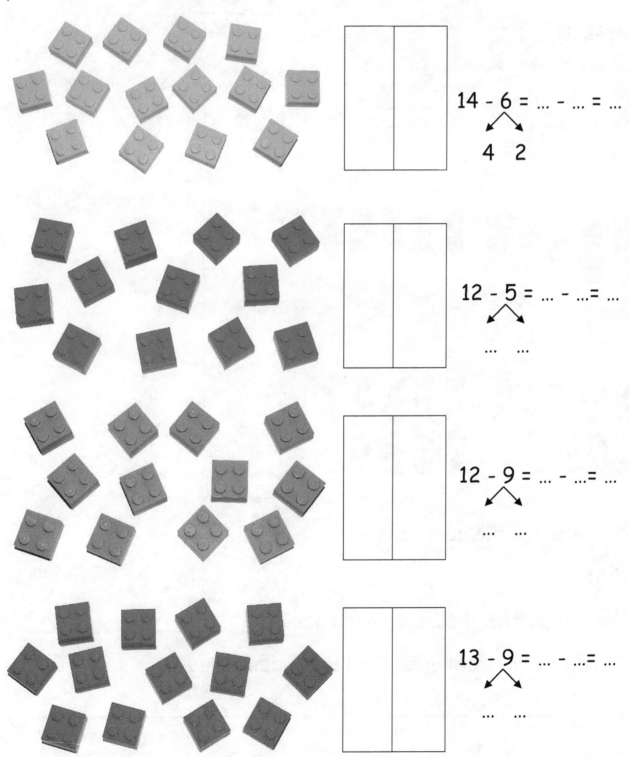

14 - 6 = ... - ... = ...
4   2

12 - 5 = ... - ...= ...
...   ...

12 - 9 = ... - ...= ...
...   ...

13 - 9 = ... - ...= ...
...   ...

www.stemmindset.com

1.   NSS. <u>Write</u> 5 number sentences with 3 or more numbers so that the sum equals 17. The first one is done for you.

2 + 6 + 5 + 4   = 17

_____   = 17

_____   = 17

_____   = 17

_____   = 17

_____   = 17

2.   NSS. <u>Fill in</u> the missing numbers to complete each number sentence. <u>Use</u> the bricks. <u>Circle</u> the bricks to show the difference. You can <u>subtract</u> the leftover bricks in any order and quantity. The first one is done for you.

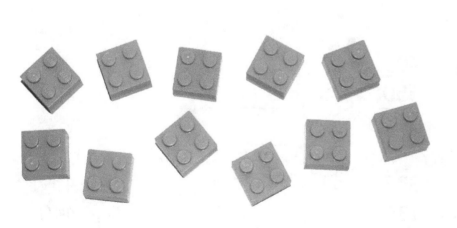

11 – 4 = 7

11 - ... - ... = 7

11 - ... - ... = 7

11 - ... - ... - ... = 7

11 - ... - ... - ... = 7

1.   NSS. <u>Write</u> addition number sentences for each picture. <u>Find</u> the value. <u>Draw</u> the white dots for the addend 1 and the black dots for the addend 2 in the box. <u>Make</u> 10 with the biggest number 😉.

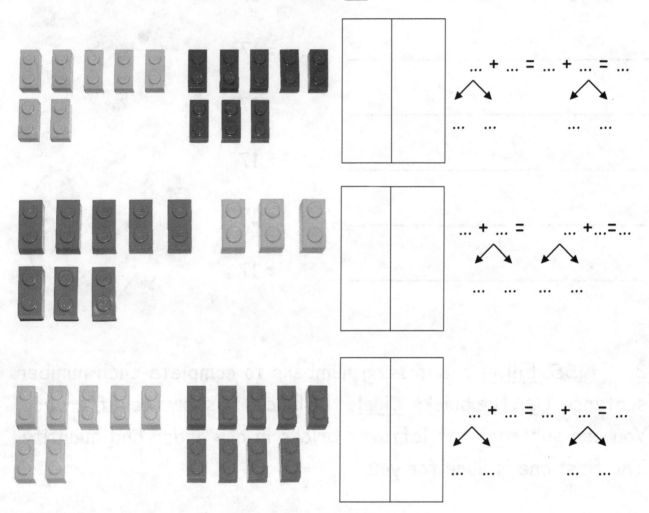

2.   NSS. <u>Find</u> the sums.

227	409	840	712
+ 131	+ 350	+ 125	+ 226
358	....	....	....

746	852	573	459
+ 212	+ 135	+ 124	+ 440
....	....	....	....

www.stemmindset.com

1. NSS. <u>Write</u> subtraction number sentences for each picture. <u>Circle</u> the bricks by 5's. <u>Find</u> the value. <u>Draw</u> the black dots for the minuend and then <u>change</u> the black dots into the white dots (or cross out the black dots) to show the subtrahend in the box.

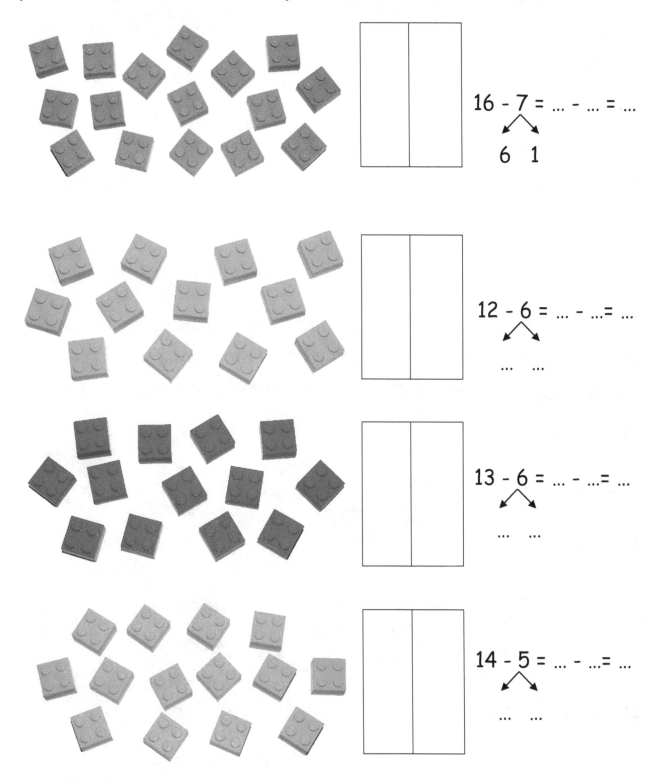

16 - 7 = … - … = …
6   1

12 - 6 = … - …= …
…   …

13 - 6 = … - …= …
…   …

14 - 5 = … - …= …
…   …

1.   NSS. <u>Find</u> the sums and <u>change</u> the addends' order. The first one is done for you.

7 + 5 + 8 = 20	8 + 7 + 5 = 20	5 + 8 + 7 = 20
6 + 3 + 7 = ...	... + ... + ... = ...	... + ... + ... = ...
4 + 2 + 9 = ...	... + ... + ... = ...	... + ... + ... = ...
3 + 2 + 6 = ...	... + ... + ... = ...	... + ... + ... = ...
9 + 1 + 7 = ...	... + ... + ... = ...	... + ... + ... = ...

2.   NSS. <u>Fill in</u> the missing numbers to complete each number sentence. <u>Use</u> the bricks. <u>Circle</u> the bricks to show the difference. You can <u>subtract</u> the leftover bricks in any order and quantity.

11 – 5 = 6

11 - ... - ... = 6

11 - ... - ... = 6

11 - ... - ... = 6

11 - ... - ... - ... = 6

11 - ... - ... - ... = 6   11 - ... - ... - ... - ... = 6

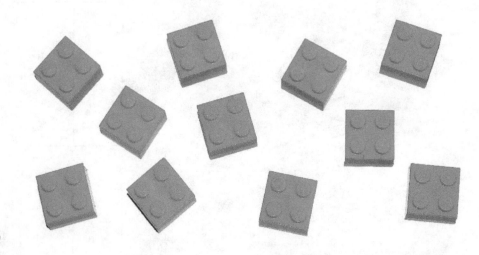

1. NSS. <u>Write</u> subtraction number sentences for each picture. <u>Circle</u> the bricks by 5's. <u>Find</u> the value. <u>Draw</u> the black dots for the minuend and then <u>change</u> the black dots into the white dots (or cross out the black dots) to show the subtrahend in the box.

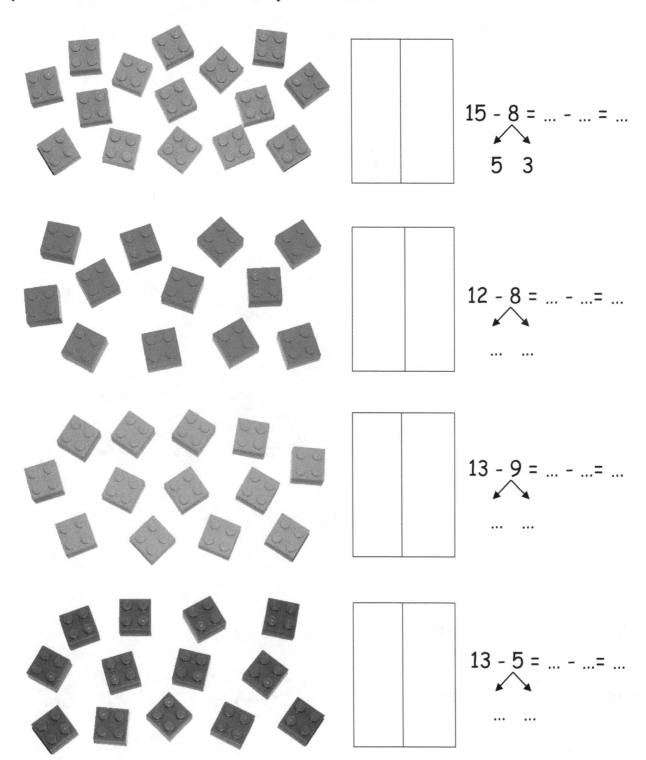

15 - 8 = ... - ... = ...

5   3

12 - 8 = ... - ... = ...

...   ...

13 - 9 = ... - ... = ...

...   ...

13 - 5 = ... - ... = ...

...   ...

1.   NSS. <u>Write</u> all addition or subtraction number sentences with 1, 2, 3, 4, 5, 6, 7, 8, 9, 10, 11, 12, 13, 15, 16, 17, 18, or 20 so <u>the sum or the difference</u> equals 14. You can <u>use</u> each number several times.

9 + 5 = 14   … + … = 14   … + … = 14

… + … = 14   … + … = 14   … + … = 14

… + … = 14   … - … = 14   … - … = 14

… - … = 14   … - … = 14

… - … = 14   … - … = 14

2.   <u>Write</u> the numbers between:

122   … …   125   539   … …   542

483   … …   486   890   … …   893

248   … …   251   965   … …   968

1. NSS. <u>Write</u> addition number sentences for each picture. <u>Find</u> the value. <u>Draw</u> the white dots for the addend 1 and the black dots for the addend 2 in the box. <u>Make</u> 10 with the biggest number 😉.

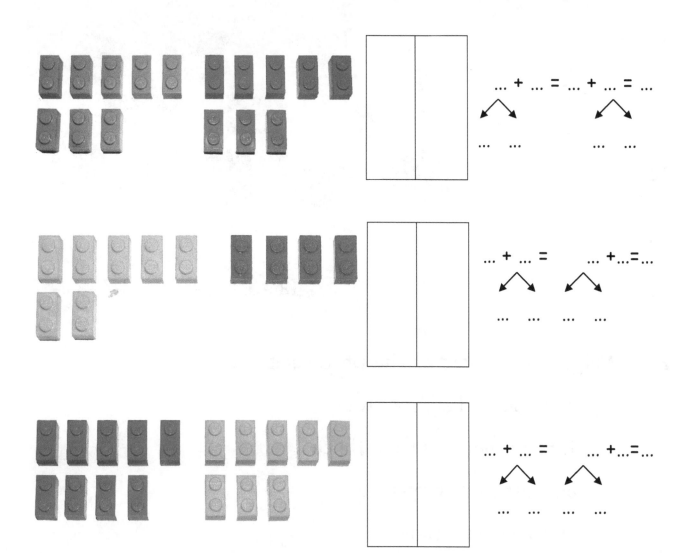

2. <u>Write</u> the numbers.

_____   four hundred seventy-four

_____   seven hundred forty-eight

_____   six hundred twenty-six

_____   nine hundred sixty-nine

1.   NSS. Fill in the missing numbers to complete each number sentence. Use the bricks. Circle the bricks to show the difference. You can subtract the leftover bricks in any order and quantity.

12 – 5 = 7

12 - ... - ... = 7

12 - ... - ... = 7

12 - ... - ... = 7

12 - ... - ... - ... = 7

12 - ... - ... - ... = 7

12 - ... - ... - ... - ... = 7

2.   Write the numbers or the word numbers.

...   two hundred eighty-five

...   three hundred ninety-three

...   one hundred fifty-seven

...   five hundred twelve

...   eight hundred thirty-one

256   _____

            _____

409   _____

962   9 _____ 6 _____ 2 _____

www.stemmindset.com

1. <u>Write</u> 5 number sentences with 3 additions and 3 subtractions so that the value equals 18. The first one is done for you.

6 + 8 - 9 + 3 + 12 – 4 + 2   = 18

_____   = 18

_____   = 18

_____   = 18

_____   = 18

_____   = 18

2. <u>Find</u> the unknown number.

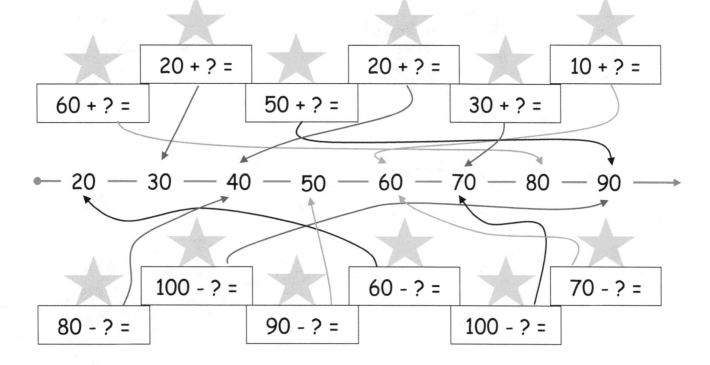

1.   NSS. <u>Write</u> addition number sentences for each picture. <u>Find</u> the value. <u>Draw</u> the white dots for the addend 1 and the black dots for the addend 2 in the box. <u>Make</u> 10 with the biggest number 😊.

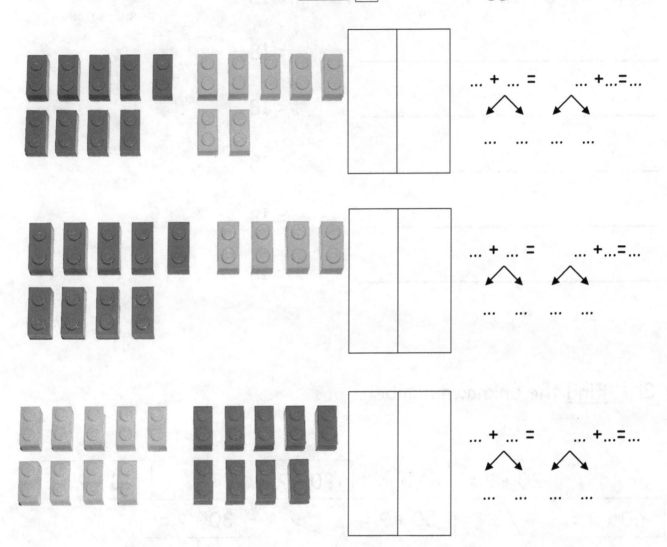

2.   <u>Write</u> the numbers between:

367	… …	370	134	… …	137
895	… …	898	471	… …	474
546	… …	549	621	… …	624

     www.stemmindset.com

1. NSS. Write 5 number sentences with 3 or more numbers so that the sum equals 19. The first one is done for you.

3 + 5 + 7 + 4   = 19

_____   = 19

_____   = 19

_____   = 19

_____   = 19

_____   = 19

2. NSS. Fill in the missing numbers to complete each number sentence. Use the bricks. Circle the bricks to show the difference. You can subtract the leftover bricks in any order and quantity.

13 – 5 = 8

13 - ... - ... = 8

13 - ... - ... = 8

13 - ... - ... = 8

13 - ... - ... - ... = 8

13 - ... - ... - ... = 8   13 - ... - ... - ... - ... = 8

1.   Compare the bricks. Write down HOW MANY MORE or LESS green bricks there are than yellow bricks. Circle the correct word (More or Less).

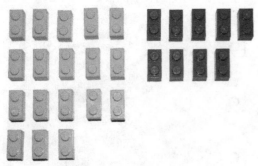

…   More or Less

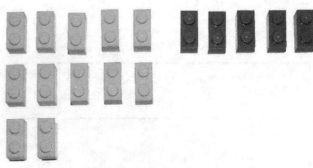

…   More or Less

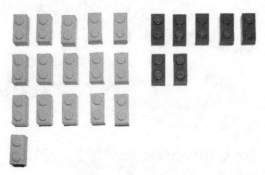

…   More or Less

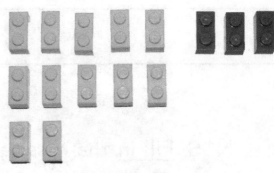

…   More or Less

2.   NSS. Fill in the missing numbers to complete each number sentence. Use the bricks. Circle the bricks to show the difference. You can subtract the leftover bricks in any order and quantity.

15 – 6 = 9

15 - … - … = 9

15 - … - … = 9

15 - … - … = 9

15 - … - … - … = 9

15 - … - … - … = 9

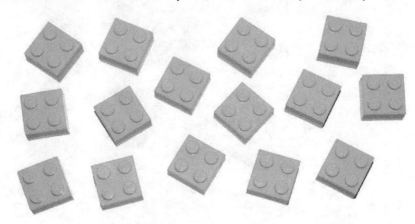

15 - … - … - … - … = 9

     www.stemmindset.com

1.   NSS. Write addition number sentences for each picture. Find the value. Draw the white dots for the addend 1 and the black dots for the addend 2 in the box. Make 10 with the biggest number 😊.

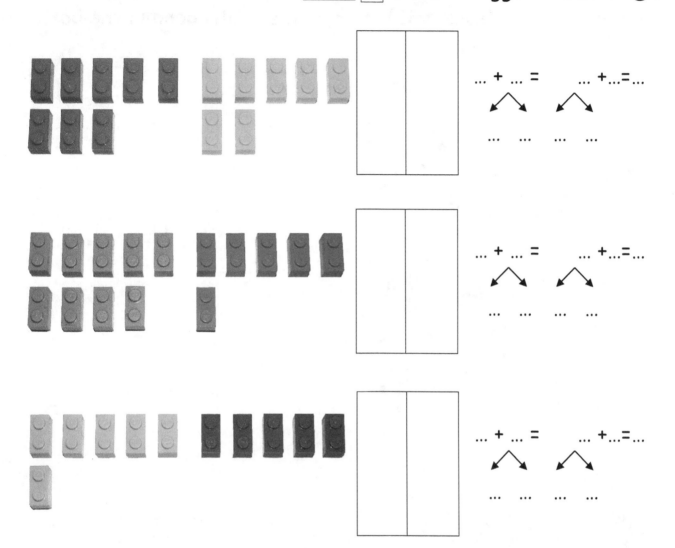

2.   Complete each number sentence. Try to make 10's as it's easier to calculate them. You can draw the arrows to help you make 10's.

17 − 3 − 1 − 6 − 1 = ...   13 − 8 − 2 − 1 − 1 = ...

20 − 4 − 5 − 4 − 5 = ...   20 − 5 − 7 − 4 − 2 = ...

15 + 4 − 13 + 6 = ...   14 − 7 + 10 − 9 = ...

12 + 5 − 11 + 4 = ...   11 − 7 + 15 − 12 = ...

1.   NSS. <u>Write</u> subtraction number sentences for each picture. <u>Circle</u> the bricks by 5's. <u>Find</u> the value. <u>Draw</u> the black dots for the minuend and then <u>change</u> the black dots into the white dots (or cross out the black dots) to show the subtrahend in the box.

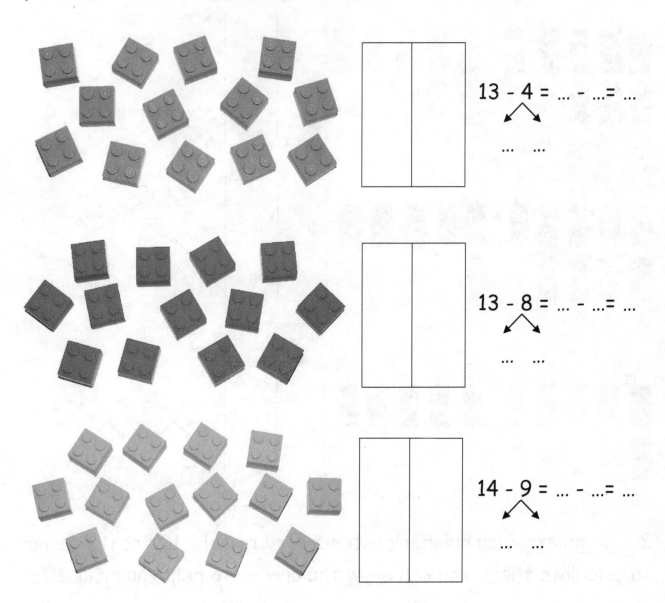

13 - 4 = ... - ...= ...
...   ...

13 - 8 = ... - ...= ...
...   ...

14 - 9 = ... - ...= ...
...   ...

2.   <u>Find</u> the value.

8527 : the sum of the ones and hundreds is _____. The difference between the thousands and tens is _____.

www.stemmindset.com

1. NSS. <u>Write</u> all addition or subtraction number sentences with 1, 2, 3, 4, 5, 6, 7, 8, 9, 10, 11, 12, 13, 14, 15, 16, 17, 18, 19, or 20 so the sum or the difference equals 15. You can use each number several times.

8 + 7 = 15   ... + ... = 15   ... - ... = 15

... + ... = 15   ... + ... = 15   ... - ... = 15

... + ... = 15   ... + ... = 15   ... - ... = 15

... + ... = 15   ... - ... = 15   ... - ... = 15

2. NSS. <u>Fill in</u> the missing numbers to complete each number sentence. <u>Use</u> the bricks. <u>Circle</u> the bricks to show the difference. You can <u>subtract</u> the leftover bricks in any order and quantity.

12 – 7 = 5

12 - ... - ... = 5

12 - ... - ... = 5

12 - ... - ... = 5

12 - ... - ... = 5

12 - ... - ... - ... = 5   12 - ... - ... - ... = 5

12 - ... - ... - ... = 5   12 - ... - ... - ... - ... = 5

12 - ... - ... - ... - ... = 5   12 - ... - ... - ... - ... - ... = 5

1.   <u>Write</u> all addition or subtraction number sentences with $\boxed{1, 2,}$ $\boxed{3, 4, 5, 6, 7, 8, 9, 10, 11, 12, 13, 14, 15, 16, 18, 19, \text{ or } 20}$ so <u>the sum</u> or <u>the difference</u> equals $\boxed{17}$. You <u>can use</u> each number several times.

… + … = 17   … + … = 17   … + … = 17

… + … = 17   … + … = 17   20 - 3 = 17

… + … = 17   … + … = 17   … - … = 17

… + … = 17   … - … = 17

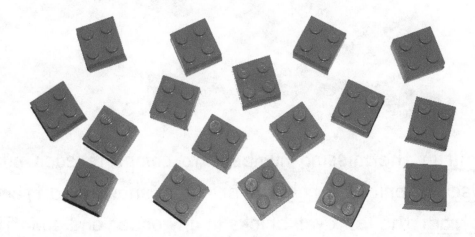

2.   <u>Find</u> the difference.

11			3
15			…
18			…
13	-	8	…
17			…
14			…
12			…
16			…

12			7
15			…
11	-	5	…
14			…
13			…

12			…
11	-	2	…

14			10
11			…
13	-	4	…
12			…

13			…
11	-	3	…
12			…

                   www.stemmindset.com

1. NSS. <u>Write</u> addition number sentences for each picture. <u>Find</u> the value. <u>Draw</u> the white dots for the addend 1 and the black dots for the addend 2 in the box. <u>Make</u> 10 with the biggest number 😊.

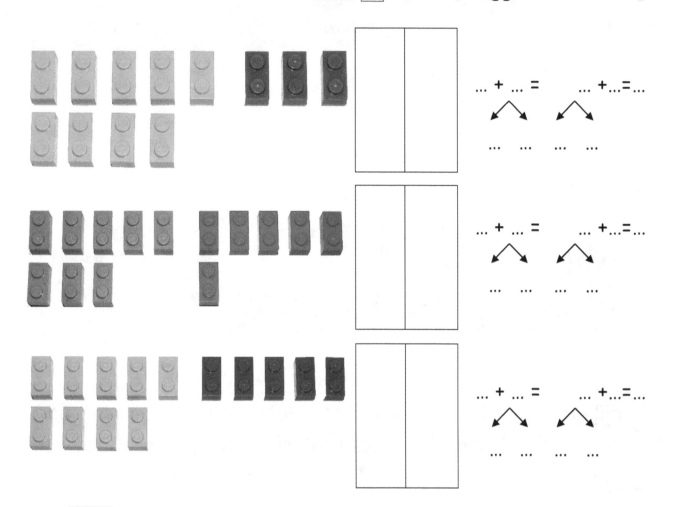

2. NSS. <u>Complete</u> each number sentence. <u>Make</u> 10's with arrows.

18 – 6 – 2 – 4 – 4 = …   15 – 1 – 7 – 3 – 1 = …

18 – 3 – 8 – 2 – 5 = …   20 – 5 – 7 – 4 – 3 = …

14 + 5 – 17 + 9 = …   13 – 8 + 12 – 6 = …

16 + 3 – 14 + 6 = …   19 – 3 + 4 – 15 = …

1.   <u>Write</u> all addition or subtraction number sentences with 1, 2, 3, 4, 5, 6, 7, 8, 9, 10, 11, 12, 13, 14, 15, 16, 17, 19, or 20 so <u>the sum or difference</u> equals 18.

15 + 3 = 18   … + … = 18   … - … = 18

… + … = 18   … + … = 18   … + … = 18

… + … = 18   … + … = 18   … - … = 18

… + … = 18   … + … = 18

2.   <u>Fill in</u> the missing numbers to complete each number sentence. <u>Use</u> the bricks. <u>Circle</u> the bricks to show the difference. You can <u>subtract</u> the leftover bricks in any order and quantity.

14 – 5 = 9

14 - … - … = 9

14 - … - … = 9

14 - … - … = 9

14 - … - … - … = 9

14 - … - … - … = 9   14 - … - … - … - … = 9

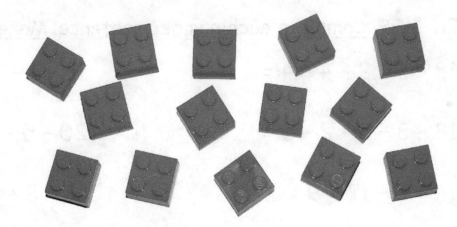

            www.stemmindset.com

1. <u>Find</u> the sums. NSS: make ten with bigger number, distribute the smaller number

5			7
9			11
2			...
7			...
4	+	2	...
10			...
3			...
6			...
1			...
8			...

10			19
6			15
2			...
4			...
9	+	9	...
5			...
3			...
1			...
7			...
8			...

2			7
10			15
8			...
4			...
3	+	5	...
7			...
1			...
9			...
6			...
5			...

2. <u>Draw</u> an arrow to connect each number sentence with its matching answer on the number line. The first one is done for you.

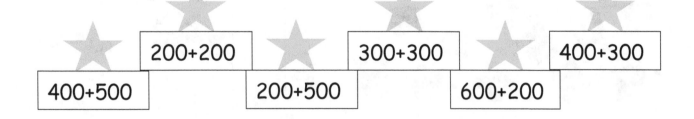

200+300   200+400   200 + 100

400+400   100 + 100   100 + 800

← 200 – 300 – 400 – 500 – 600 – 700 – 800 – 900 →

200+200   300+300   400+300

400+500   200+500   600+200

1.   NSS. <u>Write</u> subtraction number sentences for each picture. <u>Circle</u> the bricks by 5's. <u>Find</u> the value. <u>Draw</u> the black dots for the minuend and then <u>change</u> the black dots into the white dots (or cross out the black dots) to show the subtrahend in the box.

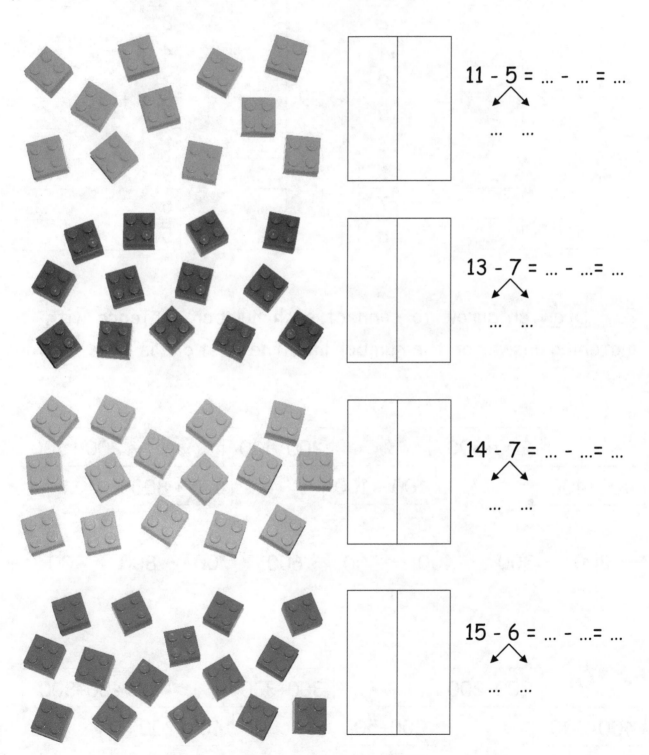

11 - 5 = ... - ... = ...

... ...

13 - 7 = ... - ...= ...

... ...

14 - 7 = ... - ...= ...

... ...

15 - 6 = ... - ...= ...

... ...

www.stemmindset.com

1. <u>Find</u> the sums. NSS: make ten with bigger number, distribute the smaller number.

5			13
9			...
2			...
7			...
4	+	8	...
10			...
3			...
6			...
1			...
8			...

10			13
6			...
2			...
4			...
9	+	3	...
5			...
3			...
1			...
7			...
8			...

2			9
10			...
8			...
4			...
3	+	7	...
7			...
1			...
9			...
6			...
5			...

2. NSS. <u>Write</u> all addition or subtraction number sentences with 1, 2, 3, 4, 5, 6, 7, 8, 9, 10, 11, 12, 13, 14, 15, 16, 17, 18, or 20 so the sum or difference equals 19. You <u>can use</u> each number several times.

... + ... = 19   ... + ... = 19

... + ... = 19   ... + ... = 19

... + ... = 19   ... + ... = 19

... + ... = 19   ... + ... = 19

... + ... = 19   ... - ... = 19

1.   NSS. <u>Write</u> subtraction number sentences for each picture. <u>Circle</u> the bricks by $\boxed{5's}$. <u>Find</u> the value. <u>Draw</u> the black dots for the minuend and then <u>change</u> the black dots into the white dots (or cross out the black dots) to show the subtrahend in the box.

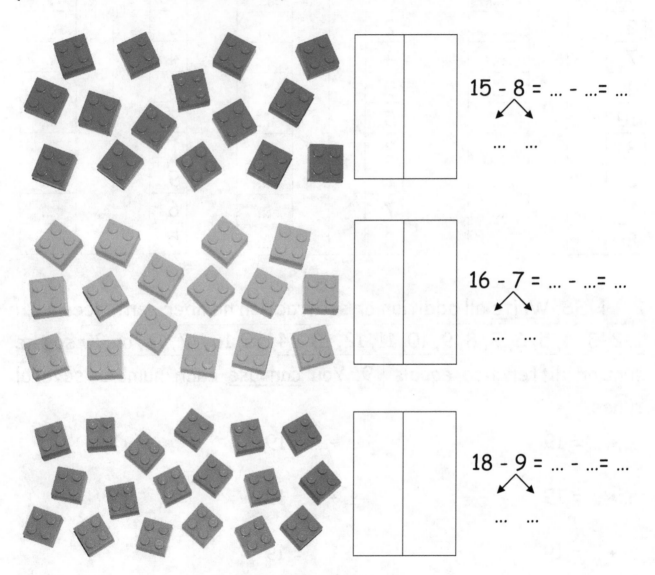

15 - 8 = … - …= …

… …

16 - 7 = … - …= …

… …

18 - 9 = … - …= …

… …

2.   <u>Continue</u> a series of numbers.

1, 2, 3, 5, _____, _____, _____, _____, _____, _____.

1. <u>Compare</u>, using >, <, =.

3 + 7	>	10 − 2	8 − 5	=	4 − 1
4 + 2	<	9 − 2	7 − 2	>	10 − 6
2 + 5	<	10 − 2	8 − 5	=	10 − 7
6 + 3	>	4 + 3	6 − 4	<	5 − 2

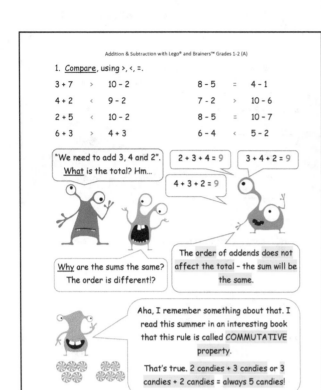

"We need to add 3, 4 and 2". <u>What</u> is the total? Hm...

2 + 3 + 4 = 9

3 + 4 + 2 = 9

4 + 3 + 2 = 9

<u>Why</u> are the sums the same? The order is different!?

The order of addends does not affect the total – the sum will be the same.

Aha, I remember something about that. I read this summer in an interesting book that this rule is called COMMUTATIVE property.

That's true. 2 candies + 3 candies or 3 candies + 2 candies = always 5 candies!

---

1. Number Sense Strategy (NSS). <u>Find</u> the sums, <u>change</u> the addends' order. The first one is done for you.

2 + 5 + 3 = 10	5 + 3 + 2 = 10	3 + 2 + 5 = 10
1 + 4 + 2 = 7	4 + 1 + 2 = 7	2 + 1 + 4 = 7
5 + 0 + 5 = 10	5 + 5 + 0 = 10	0 + 5 + 5 = 10
4 + 1 + 3 = 8	1 + 3 + 4 = 8	3 + 4 + 1 = 8
6 + 1 + 3 = 10	1 + 3 + 6 = 10	3 + 6 + 1 = 10

2. <u>Complete</u> an addition number sentence with tens and ones.

16 = 10 + 6	18 = 10 + 8	15 = 10 + 5
10 = 10 + 0	13 = 10 + 3	17 = 10 + 7
29 = 20 + 9	24 = 20 + 4	21 = 20 + 1

3. NSS. <u>Fill in</u> the missing numbers to make the comparison true.

1 + 9	=	10 − 4	9 − 4	=	7 − 2
3 + 4	=	10 − 3	10 − 6	=	1 + 3
4 + 4	=	6 + 2	6 − 5	=	8 − 7
5 − 3	=	9 − 7	3 + 3	=	10 − 4

---

1. NSS. <u>Take</u> the number of bricks you see in the picture. If you can divide (or put) bricks equally into each of 2 boxes, <u>write</u> the number of bricks you put into one box (2 = 1 + 1; 4 = 2 + 2, etc.). If you cannot divide them equally into 2 boxes (3 = 1 + 1 + 1, 5 = 2 + 2 + 1, etc.), <u>cross out</u> the picture.

1
0

I cannot divide 1 brick equally into 2 boxes, so, I cross it out and write 1 and 0.

1
1

I can put away 2 bricks equally into 2 boxes: 1 + 1, so, I write 1 and 1.

2
1

I cannot divide 3 bricks equally into 2 boxes, so, I cross it out and write 2 and 1.

2
2

I can put away 4 bricks equally into 2 boxes: 2 + 2, so, I write 2 and 2.

---

1. NSS. <u>Take</u> the number of bricks you see in the picture. If you can divide (or put) bricks equally into each of 2 boxes, <u>write</u> the number of bricks you put into one box (2 = 1 + 1; 4 = 2 + 2, etc.). If you cannot divide them equally into 2 boxes (3 = 1 + 1 + 1, 5 = 2 + 2 + 1, etc.), <u>cross out</u> the picture.

3
2

I cannot divide 5 bricks equally into 2 boxes, so, I cross it out and write 3 and 2.

3
3

I can put away 6 bricks equally into 2 boxes: 3 + 3, so, I write 3 and 3.

4
3

I cannot divide 7 bricks equally into 2 boxes, so, I cross it out and write 4 and 3.

4
4

I can put away 8 bricks equally into 2 boxes: 4 + 4, so, I write 4 and 4.

1. NSS. Take the number of bricks you see in the picture. If you can divide (or put) bricks equally into each of 2 boxes, write the number of bricks you put into one box (2 = 1 + 1; 4 = 2 + 2, etc.). If you cannot divide them equally into 2 boxes (3 = 1 + 1 + 1, 5 = 2 + 2 + 1, etc.), cross out the picture.

| 5 |
| 4 |

I cannot divide 9 bricks equally into 2 boxes, so, I cross it out and write 5 and 4.

| 5 |
| 5 |

I can put away 10 bricks equally into 2 boxes: 5 + 5, so, I write 5 and 5.

The numbers 1, 3, 5, 7, 9 are indivisible by 2. They always have 1 left over. These numbers are called ODD numbers.

The numbers 0, 2, 4, 6, 8, 10 are divisible by 2. These numbers are called EVEN numbers.

Aha, you hear right. 0 is an even number, too. Just remember this fact. We will learn about zero later, next grade.

---

1. NSS. Write 5 number sentences with 3 additions and 3 subtractions so that the value equals 10. The first one is done for you. Answers will vary.

6 + 2 - 5 + 9 + 4 - 3 - 3   = 10

_____ = 10

_____ = 10

_____ = 10

_____ = 10

_____ = 10

2. NSS. Complete each addition number sentence with tens and ones. The first one is done for you.

16 = 10 + 6   11 = 10 + 1   69 = 60 + 9

35 = 30 + 5   59 = 50 + 9   80 = 80 + 0

46 = 40 + 6   32 = 30 + 2   56 = 50 + 6

29 = 20 + 9   24 = 20 + 4   91 = 90 + 1

3. Continue a series of numbers:

5, 10, 15, 20, 25, 30, 35, 40, 45.

---

1. NSS. Find the difference.

1 4	8 2	4 3	3 1	6 9
- 4	- 2	- 3	- 1	- 9
1 0	8 0	4 0	3 0	6 0

1 9	6 7	7 8	9 5	2 9
- 2	- 5	- 4	- 3	- 8
1 7	6 2	7 4	9 2	2 1

2 5	7 1	6 8	9 2	4 7
- 1 0	- 3 0	- 3 0	- 5 0	- 1 0
1 5	4 1	3 8	4 2	3 7

2. Continue a series of numbers:

1, 4, 3, 6, 5, 8, 7, 10, 9, 12, 11, 14, 13.

3. NSS. Complete each addition number sentence with tens and ones. The first one is done for you.

24 = 20 + 4   35 = 30 + 5   82 = 80 + 2

14 = 10 + 4   97 = 90 + 7   51 = 50 + 1

47 = 40 + 7   62 = 60 + 2   35 = 30 + 5

73 = 70 + 3   45 = 40 + 5   78 = 70 + 8

NSS. Write addition number sentences for each picture. Find the value. Draw the white dots for the addend 1 and the black dots for the addend 2 in the box. Make ten with the biggest number ☺.

Addend 1 Addend 2

2 + 9 = 9 + 2 = …

Guys, I want to solve it with bricks. I take 2 yellow bricks and 9 red bricks. I prefer to put them in 5's, I like to count by 5's: 5, 10, 15, 20… It's easy. See? I like this math.

Now, I see that 9 is 5 + 4 and 1 red brick is missing. I add 1 yellow brick to make it 10: 9 + 1 = 10. 1 yellow is left: 10 + 1 = 11. I am GENIUS!

I like dots more. First, I draw 2 white dots for yellow bricks and then, add black dots for 9 red bricks. It's fun!

It's much easier to count by 5 and I count dots by 5, too. I add dots: 2 + 3 + 5 = 10 and 1 is left: 10 + 1 = 11.

2 + 9 = 9 + 2 = …

1 1   1 1

I count by 10's. If I have 9, I need 1 more up to 10. I distribute 2 into 1+1. So, 9 + 1 + 1 = 11.

NSS. <u>Write</u> addition number sentences for each picture. <u>Find</u> the value. <u>Draw</u> the white dots for the addend 1 and the black dots for the addend 2 in the box. <u>Make</u> ten with the biggest number ☺.

2 + 9 = 9 + 2 = …

2 + 9 = 9 + 2 = 11

I like numbers, too, don't I? I'm an imagination-abstraction-obsessed Brainer! And I count by 10's!

I find out the bigger number – it's 9. If I have 9, I need 1 more to make 10. I take 1 more out of 2. So, 2 = 1 + 1. And 1 + 1 + 9 = 11. Smart? Very smart! By the way, I can also write it as 9 + 1 + 1 = 11. It's up to you. What's easier for you is better.

1. NSS. <u>Complete</u> each addition number sentence with tens and ones. The first one is done for you.

16 = 10 + 6	11 = 10 + 1	19 = 10 + 9
13 = 10 + 3	18 = 10 + 8	20 = 20 + 0
23 = 20 + 3	25 = 20 + 5	28 = 20 + 8
27 = 20 + 7	29 = 20 + 9	24 = 20 + 4

---

1. NSS. <u>Find</u> the sum or difference. <u>Read</u> first <u>what</u> your Brainers say☺.

400 + 6 = 406	650 + 5 = 655	304 + 4 = 308
263 + 2 = 265	900 + 9 = 909	730 + 8 = 738
408 − 5 = 403	268 − 7 = 261	109 − 5 = 104
828 − 4 = 824	738 − 7 = 731	246 − 4 = 242

I know how to solve it! We add the digits from the right, right? See, I will be the poet!

Stop talking nonsense! You have something to say – say it!

Sure, sure. We add from the right ones + ones, tens + tens, hundreds + hundreds. We add or subtract only ones in these equations. And we leave the rest of the numbers untouched.

400 + 6 = … → You add 0 + 6 → = 406

Let's see. If I want to subtract, I always subtract from the end: ones out of ones, tens out of tens, hundreds out of hundreds. And we leave the rest of the numbers.

408 − 5 = … → You subtract 5 out of 8 → = 403

---

1. NSS. <u>Write</u> addition number sentences for each picture. <u>Find</u> the value. <u>Draw</u> the white dots for the addend 1 and the black dots for the addend 2 in the box. <u>Make</u> ten with the biggest number ☺.

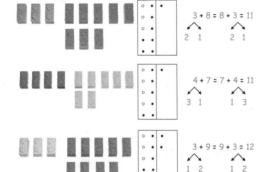

3 + 8 = 8 + 3 = 11

4 + 7 = 7 + 4 = 11

3 + 9 = 9 + 3 = 12

2. NSS. <u>Find</u> the difference or the sum.

880 − 260 = 620	490 − 170 = 320	380 − 150 = 230
970 − 530 = 440	650 − 240 = 410	760 − 640 = 120
200 + 150 = 350	500 + 370 = 870	800 + 120 = 920

---

1. NSS. <u>Write</u> all addition or subtraction number sentences with 1, 2, 3, 4, 5, 6, 7, 8, 9, 10, 11, 12, 13, 14, 15, 16, 17, 18, 19, or 20 so the sum or difference equals 13. You can <u>use</u> each number several times.

5 + 8 = 13	2 + 11 = 13
4 + 9 = 13	1 + 12 = 13
3 + 10 = 13	16 − 3 = 13
20 − 7 = 13	15 − 2 = 13
19 − 6 = 13	14 − 1 = 13
18 − 5 = 13	6 + 7 = 13
17 − 4 = 13	

2. <u>Write</u> all 2-digit numbers where the tens are 3 more than the ones: 30, 41, 52, 63, 74, 85, 96 _____
_____.

1. NSS. <u>Take</u> the number of bricks you see in the picture. If you can divide (or put) bricks equally into each of 2 boxes, <u>write</u> the number of bricks you put into one box (12 = 6 + 6; 14 = 7 + 7, etc.). If you cannot divide them equally into 2 boxes (11 = 5 + 5 + 1, 13 = 6 + 6 + 1, etc.), <u>cross out</u> the picture.

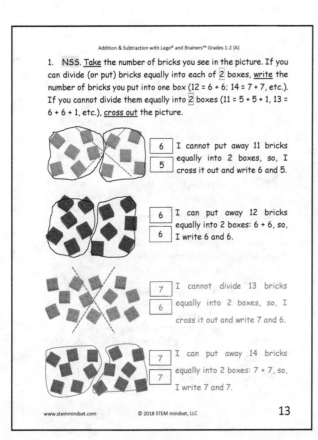

6
5
I cannot put away 11 bricks equally into 2 boxes, so, I cross it out and write 6 and 5.

6
6
I can put away 12 bricks equally into 2 boxes: 6 + 6, so, I write 6 and 6.

7
6
I cannot divide 13 bricks equally into 2 boxes, so, I cross it out and write 7 and 6.

7
7
I can put away 14 bricks equally into 2 boxes: 7 + 7, so, I write 7 and 7.

---

1. NSS. <u>Write</u> 5 number sentences with 3 or more numbers so that the sum equals 12. The first one is done for you.

4 + 3 + 3 + 2   = 12

Answers will vary.   = 12

Answers will vary.   = 12

Answers will vary.   = 12

Answers will vary.   = 12

Answers will vary.   = 12

2. NSS. <u>Find</u> the sums and <u>change</u> the addends' order. The first one is done for you. Addends will vary.

2 + 5 + 3 = 10	5 + 3 + 2 = 10	3 + 2 + 5 = 10
4 + 3 + 4 = 11	3 + 4 + 4 = 11	4 + 4 + 3 = 11
5 + 2 + 3 = 10	2 + 3 + 5 = 10	3 + 5 + 2 = 10
6 + 2 + 3 = 11	2 + 3 + 6 = 11	3 + 2 + 6 = 11
5 + 4 + 1 = 10	1 + 5 + 4 = 10	4 + 1 + 5 = 10

---

1. NSS. <u>Take</u> the number of bricks you see in the picture. If you can divide (or put) bricks equally into each of 2 boxes, <u>write</u> the number of bricks you put into one box (12 = 6 + 6; 14 = 7 + 7, etc.). If you cannot divide them equally into 2 boxes (11 = 5 + 5 + 1, 13 = 6 + 6 + 1, etc.), <u>cross out</u> the picture.

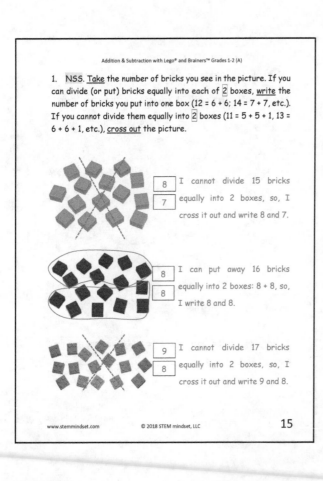

8
7
I cannot divide 15 bricks equally into 2 boxes, so, I cross it out and write 8 and 7.

8
8
I can put away 16 bricks equally into 2 boxes: 8 + 8, so, I write 8 and 8.

9
8
I cannot divide 17 bricks equally into 2 boxes, so, I cross it out and write 9 and 8.

---

1. NSS. <u>Take</u> the number of bricks you see in the picture. If you can divide (or put) bricks equally into each of 2 boxes, <u>write</u> the number of bricks you put into one box (12 = 6 + 6; 14 = 7 + 7, etc.). If you cannot divide them equally into 2 boxes (11 = 5 + 5 + 1, 13 = 6 + 6 + 1, etc.), <u>cross out</u> the picture.

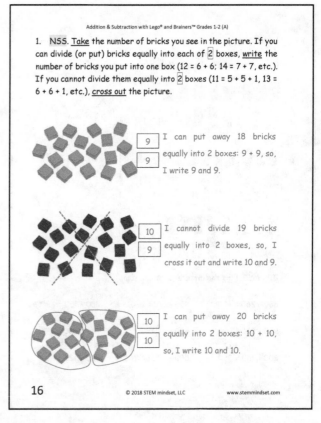

9
9
I can put away 18 bricks equally into 2 boxes: 9 + 9, so, I write 9 and 9.

10
9
I cannot divide 19 bricks equally into 2 boxes, so, I cross it out and write 10 and 9.

10
10
I can put away 20 bricks equally into 2 boxes: 10 + 10, so, I write 10 and 10.

The numbers 11, 13, 15, 17, 19 are indivisible by 2. They always have 1 in the remainder (the number that is left over.) These numbers are called ODD numbers.

The numbers 12, 14, 16, 18, 20 are divisible by 2. These numbers are called EVEN numbers.

1. NSS. Find the difference.

3 5	7 2	5 4	6 8	8 7
- 5	- 2	- 4	- 8	- 7
3 0	7 0	5 0	6 0	8 0

3 5	7 7	6 4	8 2	4 9
- 4	- 2	- 3	- 1	- 5
3 1	7 5	6 1	8 1	4 4

6 5	9 3	5 7	3 9	8 1
- 4 0	- 2 0	- 1 0	- 2 0	- 7 0
2 5	7 3	4 7	1 9	1 1

2. Cross out the bee which is different.

---

1. NSS. Write addition number sentences for each picture. Find the value. Draw the white dots for the addend 1 and the black dots for the addend 2 in the box. Make ten with the biggest number ☺.

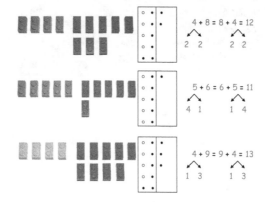

$4 + 8 = 8 + 4 = 12$

$5 + 6 = 6 + 5 = 11$

$4 + 9 = 9 + 4 = 13$

2. The sum of 2 2-digit numbers is 50. Their difference is 30. What are these 2-digit numbers?

Answer: 40 and 10.

$40 + 10 = 50$ $40 - 10 = 30$

---

1. NSS. Write subtraction number sentences for each picture. Circle the bricks by 5's. Find the value. Draw the black dots for the minuend and then change the black dots into the white dots to show the subtrahend in the box. Cross out how many bricks you subtract.

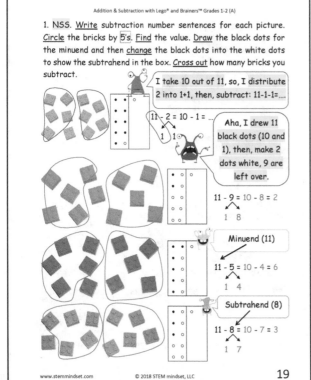

I take 10 out of 11, so, I distribute 2 into 1+1, then, subtract: 11-1-1=....

$11 - 2 = 10 - 1 = ...$

Aha, I drew 11 black dots (10 and 1), then, make 2 dots white, 9 are left over.

$11 - 9 = 10 - 8 = 2$

Minuend (11)

$11 - 5 = 10 - 4 = 6$

Subtrahend (8)

$11 - 8 = 10 - 7 = 3$

---

1. NSS. Write addition number sentences for each picture. Find the value. Draw the white dots for the addend 1 and the black dots for the addend 2 in the box. Make ten with the biggest number ☺.

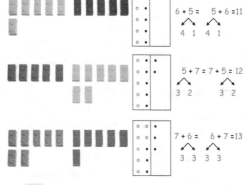

$6 + 5 =$ $5 + 6 = 11$

$5 + 7 = 7 + 5 = 12$

$7 + 6 =$ $6 + 7 = 13$

2. NSS. Find the sums.

200 + 300 = 500	400 + 600 = 1000	500 + 500 = 1000
100 + 600 = 700	200 + 700 = 900	400 + 300 = 700
500 + 400 = 900	800 + 200 = 1000	300 + 300 = 600
400 + 400 = 800	200 + 600 = 800	100 + 900 = 1000
200 + 500 = 700	400 + 200 = 600	500 + 400 = 900

1. NSS. <u>Fill in</u> the missing numbers to complete each number sentence. <u>Use</u> the bricks. <u>Circle</u> the bricks to show the difference. *Answers will vary.*

11 – 7 = 4

> I circle 4 bricks, 7 are left over. I can arrange them in many ways: 3+4, 2+5, 1+2+3+1.

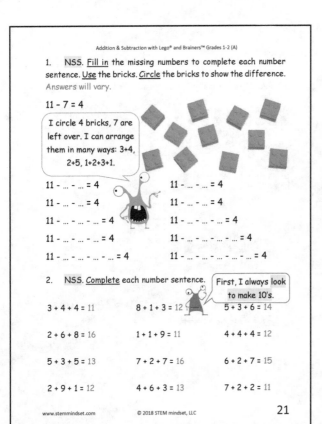

11 – ... – ... = 4   11 – ... – ... = 4

11 – ... – ... = 4   11 – ... – ... = 4

11 – ... – ... – ... = 4   11 – ... – ... = 4

11 – ... – ... – ... = 4   11 – ... – ... – ... = 4

11 – ... – ... – ... – ... = 4   11 – ... – ... – ... – ... = 4

2. NSS. <u>Complete</u> each number sentence.

> First, I always look to make 10's.

3 + 4 + 4 = 11   8 + 1 + 3 = 12   5 + 3 + 6 = 14

2 + 6 + 8 = 16   1 + 1 + 9 = 11   4 + 4 + 4 = 12

5 + 3 + 5 = 13   7 + 2 + 7 = 16   6 + 2 + 7 = 15

2 + 9 + 1 = 12   4 + 6 + 3 = 13   7 + 2 + 2 = 11

---

1. NSS. <u>Fill in</u> the missing numbers to complete each number sentence. <u>Use</u> the bricks. <u>Circle</u> the bricks to show the difference. *Answers will vary.*

13 – 4 = 7

13 – ... – ... = 7

13 – ... – ... = 7

13 – ... – ... – ... = 7

13 – ... – ... – ... – ... = 7

2. <u>Write</u> [4] number sentences with [3] additions and [3] subtractions so that the value equals [14]. *Answers will vary.*

4 + 5 – 3 + 7 + 6 – 2 – 3   = 14

_____   = 14

_____   = 14

_____   = 14

_____   = 14

---

1. NSS. <u>Write</u> subtraction number sentences for each picture. <u>Circle</u> the bricks by [5]'s. <u>Find</u> the value. <u>Draw</u> the black dots for the minuend and then <u>change</u> the black dots into the white dots (or cross out the black dots) to show the subtrahend in the box.

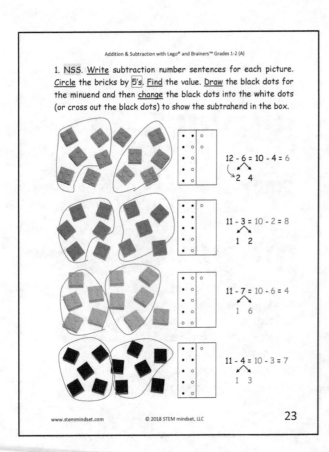

12 – 6 = 10 – 4 = 6
            2   4

11 – 3 = 10 – 2 = 8
            1   2

11 – 7 = 10 – 6 = 4
            1   6

11 – 4 = 10 – 3 = 7
            1   3

---

1. NSS. <u>Write</u> addition number sentences for each picture. <u>Find</u> the value. <u>Draw</u> the white dots for the addend 1 and the black dots for the addend 2 in the box. <u>Make</u> ten with the biggest number ☺.

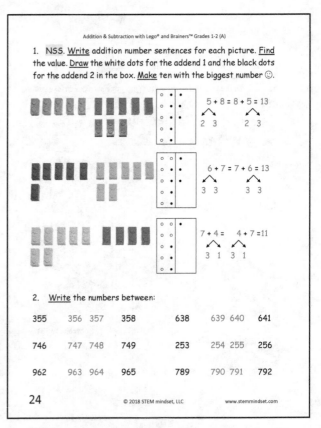

5 + 8 = 8 + 5 = 13
   2 3   2 3

6 + 7 = 7 + 6 = 13
   3 3   3 3

7 + 4 =   4 + 7 = 11
   3 1   3 1

2. <u>Write</u> the numbers between:

355	356	357	358	638	639	640	641
746	747	748	749	253	254	255	256
962	963	964	965	789	790	791	792

1. NSS. <u>Write</u> subtraction number sentences for each picture. <u>Circle</u> the bricks by 5's. <u>Find</u> the value. <u>Draw</u> the black dots for the minuend and then <u>change</u> the black dots into the white dots (or cross out the black dots) to show the subtrahend in the box.

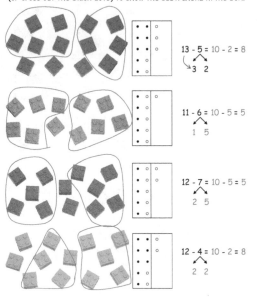

13 - 5 = 10 - 2 = 8
            3   2

11 - 6 = 10 - 5 = 5
            1   5

12 - 7 = 10 - 5 = 5
            2   5

12 - 4 = 10 - 2 = 8
            2   2

---

1. NSS. <u>Write</u> addition number sentences for each picture. <u>Find</u> the value. <u>Draw</u> the white dots for the addend 1 and the black dots for the addend 2 in the box. <u>Make</u> ten with the biggest number ☺.

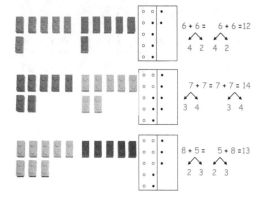

6 + 6 =   6 + 6 =12
  ∧   ∧
  4 2   4 2

7 + 7 = 7 = 7 + 7 = 14
  ∧   ∧
  3 4   3 4

8 + 5 =   5 + 8 =13
  ∧   ∧
  2 3   2 3

2. The sum of ☐2 numbers is ☐19. Their difference is ☐3. <u>What</u> are these 2 numbers?

Answer: 11 and 8.

11 + 8 = 19   11 - 8 = 3

---

1. Continue a series of numbers.

2, 4, 7, 11, <u>16, 22, 29, 37, 46, 56</u>

1, 6, 9, 14, 17, 22, 25, 30, 33, 38, 41

2. Fill in the signs "+" or "-" to make the number sentences true.

9 + 7 + 5 = 21   9 - 7 + 5 = 7

7 - 5 + 9 = 11   5 + 9 - 7 = 7

3. NSS. <u>Write</u> addition or subtraction number sentences with ☐1, ☐2, 3, 4, 5, 6, 7, 8, 9, 10, 11, 12, 13, 14, 15, 17, 18, or 20 so <u>the sum or the difference</u> equals ☐16. You <u>can</u> use each number several times.

7 + 9 = 16   3 + 13 = 16

1 + 15 = 16   4 + 12 = 16

2 + 14 = 16   5 + 11 = 16

20 - 4 = 16   17 - 1 = 16

19 - 3 = 16   6 + 10 = 16

18 - 2 = 16   8 + 8 = 16

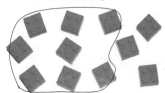

---

1. NSS. <u>Fill in</u> the missing numbers to complete each number sentence. <u>Use</u> the bricks. <u>Circle</u> the bricks to show the difference. You can <u>subtract</u> the leftover bricks in any order and quantity. The first one is done for you.

Difference

11 - 3 = 8

11 - 1 - 2 = 8

11 - 2 - 1 = 8

11 - 1 - 1 - 1 = 8

2. NSS. <u>Find</u> the value. <u>Do you notice</u> something interesting or weird about these problems?

| 11 - 5 + 6 = 12 | 14 - 7 + 6 = 13 |
| 11 - 6 + 5 = 10 | 14 - 6 + 7 = 15 |

| 15 - 5 + 6 = 16 | 13 - 5 + 6 = 14 |
| 15 - 6 + 5 = 14 | 13 - 6 + 5 = 12 |

I've noticed that <u>the numbers are the same in each equation in the box (like, 11, 5, and 6), but a different order of addition and subtraction always changes the total by 2; Answers may vary</u>.

1.   There are [10] bricks of each color. [Make] as many number sentences with the sets of tens (10, 20, 30, 40, etc.).

Answers will vary.

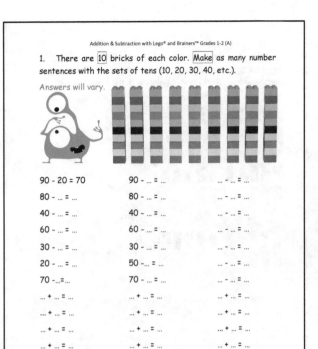

90 - 20 = 70   90 - ... = ... - ... = ...

80 - ... = ...   80 - ... = ... - ... = ...

40 - ... = ...   40 - ... = ... - ... = ...

60 - ... = ...   60 - ... = ... - ... = ...

30 - ... = ...   30 - ... = ... - ... = ...

20 - ... = ...   50 - ... = ... + ... = ...

70 - ...=...   70 - ... = ... + ... = ...

... + ... = ... + ... = ... + ... = ...

... + ... = ... + ... = ... + ... = ...

... + ... = ... + ... = ... + ... = ...

... + ... = ... + ... = ... + ... = ...

... + ... = ... + ... = ... + ... = ...

---

1.   [Write] 5 number sentences with [3] additions and [3] subtractions so that the value equals [16]. Answers will vary.

2 + 7 - 4 + 8 + 7 - 1 - 3   = 16

_____   = 16

_____   = 16

_____   = 16

_____   = 16

_____   = 16

2.   NSS. [Fill in] the missing numbers to complete each number sentence. [Use] the bricks. [Circle] the bricks to show the difference. You can [subtract] the leftover bricks in any order and quantity. The first one is done for you. Answers will vary.

Difference

12 - 3 = 9

12 - ... - ... = 9

12 - ... - ... = 9

12 - ... - ... - ... = 9

---

1.   NSS. [Fill in] the missing numbers to complete each number sentence. [Use] the bricks. [Circle] the bricks to show the difference. You can [subtract] the leftover bricks in any order and quantity. The first one is done for you. Answers will vary.

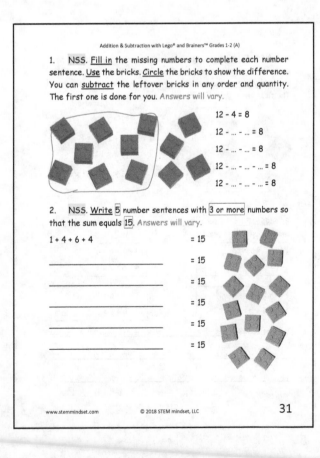

12 - 4 = 8

12 - ... - ... = 8

12 - ... - ... = 8

12 - ... - ... - ... = 8

12 - ... - ... - ... = 8

2.   NSS. [Write] 5 number sentences with [3 or more] numbers so that the sum equals [15]. Answers will vary.

1 + 4 + 6 + 4   = 15

_____   = 15

_____   = 15

_____   = 15

_____   = 15

_____   = 15

---

1.   [Draw] an arrow to connect each number sentence with its matching answer on the number line. The first one is done for you.

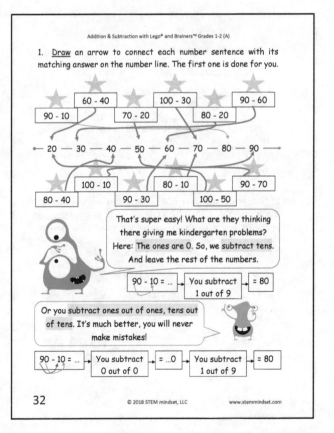

| 60 - 40 | | 100 - 30 | | 90 - 60 |

| 90 - 10 | | 70 - 20 | | 80 - 20 |

20 — 30 — 40 — 50 — 60 — 70 — 80 — 90

| 100 - 10 | | 80 - 10 | | 90 - 70 |

| 80 - 40 | | 90 - 30 | | 100 - 50 |

That's super easy! What are they thinking there giving me kindergarten problems? Here: The ones are 0. So, we subtract tens. And leave the rest of the numbers.

90 - 10 = ... → You subtract 1 out of 9 → = 80

Or you subtract ones out of ones, tens out of tens. It's much better, you will never make mistakes!

90 - 10 = ... → You subtract 0 out of 0 → = ...0 → You subtract 1 out of 9 → = 80

1. NSS. <u>Write</u> addition number sentences for each picture. <u>Find</u> the value. <u>Draw</u> the white dots for the addend 1 and the black dots for the addend 2 in the box. <u>Make</u> ten with the biggest number ☺.

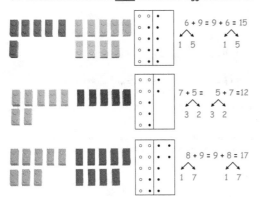

6 + 9 = 9 + 6 = 15

7 + 5 = 5 + 7 = 12

8 + 9 = 9 + 8 = 17

2. <u>Answer</u> the questions.

9361:

The sum of the thousands and ones is 9 + 1 = 10 .

The difference between the tens and hundreds is

6 - 3 = 3 .

1. NSS. <u>Write</u> subtraction number sentences for each picture. Circle the bricks by 5's. <u>Find</u> the value. <u>Draw</u> the black dots for the minuend and then <u>change</u> the black dots into the white dots (or cross out the black dots) to show the subtrahend in the box.

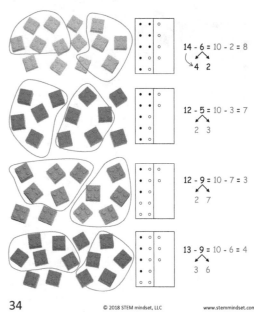

14 - 6 = 10 - 2 = 8

12 - 5 = 10 - 3 = 7

12 - 9 = 10 - 7 = 3

13 - 9 = 10 - 6 = 4

1. NSS. <u>Write</u> 5 number sentences with 3 or more numbers so that the sum equals 17. Answers will vary.

2 + 6 + 5 + 4 = 17

_____ = 17

_____ = 17

_____ = 17

_____ = 17

_____ = 17

2. NSS. <u>Fill in</u> the missing numbers to complete each number sentence. <u>Use</u> the bricks. <u>Circle</u> the bricks to show the difference. You can <u>subtract</u> the leftover bricks in any order and quantity. Answers will vary.

11 - 4 = 7

11 - ... - ... = 7

11 - ... - ... = 7

11 - ... - ... - ... = 7

11 - ... - ... - ... = 7

1. NSS. <u>Write</u> addition number sentences for each picture. <u>Find</u> the value. <u>Draw</u> the white dots for the addend 1 and the black dots for the addend 2 in the box. <u>Make</u> ten with the biggest number ☺.

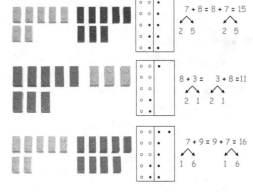

7 + 8 = 8 + 7 = 15

8 + 3 = 3 + 8 = 11

7 + 9 = 9 + 7 = 16

2. NSS. <u>Find</u> the sums.

227	409	840	712
+ 131	+ 350	+ 125	+ 226
358	759	965	938

746	852	573	459
+ 212	+ 135	+ 124	+ 440
958	987	697	899

1. NSS. <u>Write</u> subtraction number sentences for each picture. <u>Circle</u> the bricks by 5's. <u>Find</u> the value. <u>Draw</u> the black dots for the minuend and then <u>change</u> the black dots into the white dots (or cross out the black dots) to show the subtrahend in the box.

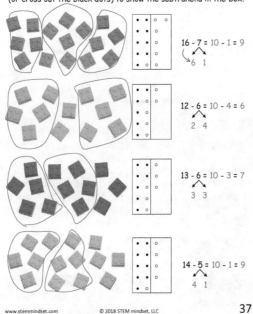

16 - 7 = 10 - 1 = 9
6 1

12 - 6 = 10 - 4 = 6
2 4

13 - 6 = 10 - 3 = 7
3 3

14 - 5 = 10 - 1 = 9
4 1

---

1. NSS. <u>Find</u> the sums and <u>change</u> the addends' order. The first one is done for you.

7 + 5 + 8 = 20	8 + 7 + 5 = 20	5 + 8 + 7 = 20
6 + 3 + 7 = 16	3 + 7 + 6 = 16	7 + 6 + 3 = 16
4 + 2 + 9 = 15	2 + 9 + 4 = 15	9 + 4 + 2 = 15
3 + 2 + 6 = 11	2 + 6 + 3 = 11	6 + 3 + 2 = 11
9 + 1 + 7 = 17	1 + 7 + 9 = 17	7 + 9 + 1 = 17

2. NSS. <u>Fill in</u> the missing numbers to complete each number sentence. <u>Use</u> the bricks. <u>Circle</u> the bricks to show the difference. Answers will vary.

11 - 5 = 6

11 - ... - ... = 6

11 - ... - ... = 6

11 - ... - ... = 6

11 - ... - ... - ... = 6

11 - ... - ... - ... = 6   11 - ... - ... - ... - ... = 6

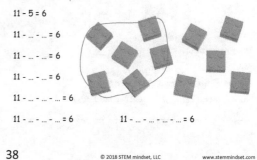

---

1. NSS. <u>Write</u> subtraction number sentences for each picture. <u>Circle</u> the bricks by 5's. <u>Find</u> the value. <u>Draw</u> the black dots for the minuend and then <u>change</u> the black dots into the white dots (or cross out the black dots) to show the subtrahend in the box.

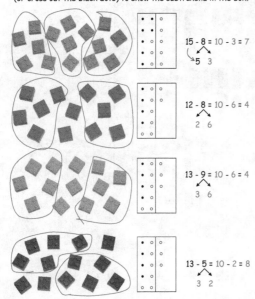

15 - 8 = 10 - 3 = 7
5 3

12 - 8 = 10 - 6 = 4
2 6

13 - 9 = 10 - 6 = 4
3 6

13 - 5 = 10 - 2 = 8
3 2

---

1. NSS. <u>Write</u> all addition or subtraction number sentences with 1, 2, 3, 4, 5, 6, 7, 8, 9, 10, 11, 12, 13, 15, 16, 17, 18, or 20 so <u>the sum or the difference</u> equals 14. You can <u>use</u> each number several times.

9 + 5 = 14	3 + 11 = 14	6 + 8 = 14
1 + 13 = 14	4 + 10 = 14	7 + 7 = 14
2 + 12 = 14	18 - 4 = 14	15 - 1 = 14
20 - 6 = 14	17 - 3 = 14	
19 - 5 = 14	16 - 2 = 14	

2. <u>Write</u> the numbers between:

122	123	124	125		539	540	541	542
483	484	485	486		890	891	892	893
248	249	250	251		965	966	967	968

1. NSS. <u>Write</u> addition number sentences for each picture. <u>Find</u> the value. <u>Draw</u> the white dots for the addend 1 and the black dots for the addend 2 in the box. <u>Make</u> ten with the biggest number ☺.

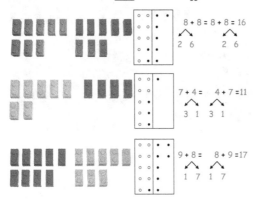

8 + 8 = 8 + 8 = 16
2 6   2 6

7 + 4 =   4 + 7 = 11
3 1   3 1

9 + 8 =   8 + 9 = 17
1 7   1 7

2. <u>Write</u> the numbers.

474	four hundred seventy-four
748	seven hundred forty-eight
626	six hundred twenty-six
969	nine hundred sixty-nine

---

1. NSS. <u>Fill in</u> the missing numbers to complete each number sentence. <u>Use</u> the bricks. <u>Circle</u> the bricks to show the difference. *Answers will vary.*

12 - 5 = 7
12 - ... - ... = 7
12 - ... - ... = 7
12 - ... - ... = 7

12 - ... - ... - ... = 7
12 - ... - ... - ... = 7

12 - ... - ... - ... - ... = 7

2. <u>Write</u> the numbers or the word numbers.

285	two hundred eighty-five
393	three hundred ninety-three
157	one hundred fifty-seven
512	five hundred twelve
831	eight hundred thirty-one
256	*two hundred fifty-six* _____
	_____
409	*four hundred nine* _____
962	9 *hundreds* _____ 6 *tens* _____ 2 *ones*

---

1. <u>Write</u> 5 number sentences with 3 additions and 3 subtractions so that the value equals 18. *Answers will vary.*

6 + 8 - 9 + 3 + 12 - 4 + 2   = 18

_____ = 18

_____ = 18

_____ = 18

_____ = 18

_____ = 18

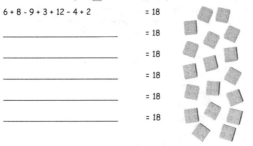

2. <u>Find</u> the unknown number.

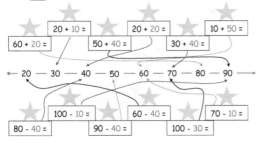

20 + 10 =   20 + 20 =   10 + 50 =
60 + 20 =   50 + 40 =   30 + 40 =

← 20 — 30 — 40 — 50 — 60 — 70 — 80 — 90 →

100 - 10 =   60 - 40 =   70 - 10 =
80 - 40 =   90 - 40 =   100 - 30 =

---

1. NSS. <u>Write</u> addition number sentences for each picture. <u>Find</u> the value. <u>Draw</u> the white dots for the addend 1 and the black dots for the addend 2 in the box. <u>Make</u> ten with the biggest number ☺.

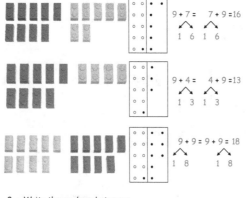

9 + 7 =   7 + 9 = 16
1 6   1 6

9 + 4 =   4 + 9 = 13
1 3   1 3

9 + 9 = 9 + 9 = 18
1 8   1 8

2. <u>Write</u> the numbers between:

367	368 369	370	134	135 136	137
895	896 897	898	471	472 473	474
546	547 548	549	621	622 623	624

1. NSS. Write 5 number sentences with 3 or more numbers so that the sum equals 19. Answers will vary.

3 + 5 + 7 + 4 _____ = 19

_____ = 19

_____ = 19

_____ = 19

_____ = 19

_____ = 19

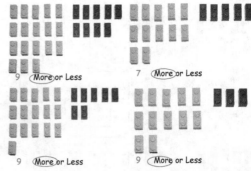

2. NSS. Fill in the missing numbers to complete each number sentence. Use the bricks. Circle the bricks to show the difference. Answers will vary.

13 – 5 = 8

13 – ... – ... = 8

13 – ... – ... = 8

13 – ... – ... = 8

13 – ... – ... – ... = 8

13 – ... – ... – ... = 8

13 – ... – ... – ... – ... = 8

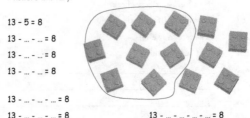

---

1. Compare the bricks. Write down HOW MANY MORE or LESS green bricks there are than yellow bricks. Circle the correct word (More or Less).

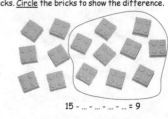

9   (More) or Less   7   (More) or Less

9   (More) or Less   9   More or (Less)

2. NSS. Fill in the missing numbers to complete each number sentence. Use the bricks. Circle the bricks to show the difference. Answers will vary.

15 – 6 = 9

15 – ... – ... = 9

15 – ... – ... = 9

15 – ... – ... = 9

15 – ... – ... – ... = 9

15 – ... – ... – ... = 9

15 – ... – ... – ... – ... = 9

---

1. NSS. Write addition number sentences for each picture. Find the value. Draw the white dots for the addend 1 and the black dots for the addend 2 in the box. Make ten with the biggest number ☺.

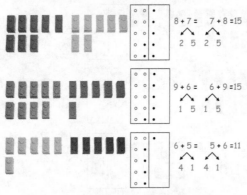

8 + 7 =   7 + 8 = 15
  2 5   2 5

9 + 6 =   6 + 9 = 15
  1 5   1 5

6 + 5 =   5 + 6 = 11
  4 1   4 1

2. Complete each number sentence. Try to make 10's as it's easier to calculate them. You can draw the arrows to help you make 10's.

17 – 3 – 1 – 6 – 1 = 6   13 – 8 – 2 – 1 – 1 = 1

20 – 4 – 5 – 4 – 5 = 2   20 – 5 – 7 – 4 – 2 = 2

15 + 4 – 13 + 6 = 12   14 – 7 + 10 – 9 = 8

12 + 5 – 11 + 4 = 10   11 – 7 + 15 – 12 = 7

---

1. NSS. Write subtraction number sentences for each picture. Circle the bricks by 5's. Find the value. Draw the black dots for the minuend and then change the black dots into the white dots (or cross out the black dots) to show the subtrahend in the box.

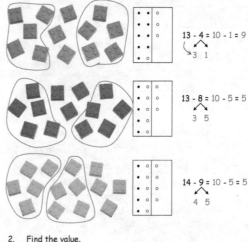

13 – 4 = 10 – 1 = 9
       3   1

13 – 8 = 10 – 5 = 5
       3   5

14 – 9 = 10 – 5 = 5
       4   5

2. Find the value.

8527: the sum of the ones and hundreds is _7 + 5 = 12____. The difference between the thousands and tens is _8 – 2 = 6____.

1. NSS. Write all addition or subtraction number sentences with 1, 2, 3, 4, 5, 6, 7, 8, 9, 10, 11, 12, 13, 14, 15, 16, 17, 18, 19, or 20 so the sum or the difference equals 15. You can use each number several times.

8 + 7 = 15	4 + 11 = 15	17 - 2 = 15
1 + 14 = 15	5 + 10 = 15	16 - 1 = 15
2 + 13 = 15	6 + 9 = 15	3 + 12 = 15
19 - 4 = 15	20 - 5 = 15	18 - 3 = 15

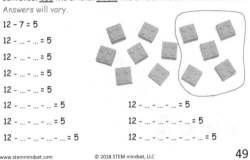

2. NSS. Fill in the missing numbers to complete each number sentence. Use the bricks. Circle the bricks to show the difference. Answers will vary.

12 - 7 = 5

12 - ... - ... = 5

12 - ... - ... = 5

12 - ... - ... = 5

12 - ... - ... = 5

12 - ... - ... - ... = 5   12 - ... - ... - ... = 5

12 - ... - ... - ... = 5   12 - ... - ... - ... = 5

12 - ... - ... - ... - ... = 5   12 - ... - ... - ... - ... - ... = 5

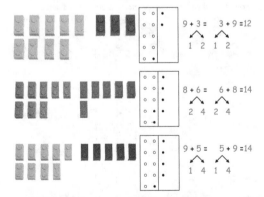

---

1. Write all addition or subtraction number sentences with 1, 2, 3, 4, 5, 6, 7, 8, 9, 10, 11, 12, 13, 14, 15, 16, 18, 19, or 20 so the sum or the difference equals 17. You can use each number several times.

1 + 16 = 17	4 + 13 = 17	6 + 11 = 17
2 + 15 = 17	5 + 12 = 17	20 - 3 = 17
3 + 14 = 17	8 + 9 = 17	19 - 2 = 17
7 + 10 = 17	18 - 1 = 17	

2. Find the difference.

11		3
15		7
18		10
13	- 8	5
17		6
14		4
12		
16		8

12		7
15		10
11	- 5	6
14		9
13		8

12	- 2	10
11		9

14		10
11	- 4	7
13		9
12		8

13	- 3	10
11		8
12		9

---

1. NSS. Write addition number sentences for each picture. Find the value. Draw the white dots for the addend 1 and the black dots for the addend 2 in the box. Make ten with the biggest number ☺.

9 + 3 =   3 + 9 = 12
          1 2   1 2

8 + 6 =   6 + 8 = 14
          2 4   2 4

9 + 5 =   5 + 9 = 14
          1 4   1 4

2. NSS. Complete each number sentence. Make 10's with arrows.

18 - 6 - 2 - 4 - 4 = 2	15 - 1 - 7 - 3 - 1 = 3
18 - 3 - 8 - 2 - 5 = 0	20 - 5 - 7 - 4 - 3 = 1
14 + 5 - 17 + 9 = 11	13 - 8 + 12 - 6 = 11
16 + 3 - 14 + 6 = 11	19 - 3 + 4 - 15 = 5

---

1. Write all addition or subtraction number sentences with 1, 2, 3, 4, 5, 6, 7, 8, 9, 10, 11, 12, 13, 14, 15, 16, 17, 19, or 20 so the sum or difference equals 18.

15 + 3 = 18	5 + 13 = 18	19 - 1 = 18
1 + 17 = 18	6 + 12 = 18	9 + 9 = 18
2 + 16 = 18	7 + 11 = 18	20 - 2 = 18
4 + 14 = 18	8 + 10 = 18	

2. Fill in the missing numbers to complete each number sentence. Use the bricks. Circle the bricks to show the difference. Answers will vary.

14 - 5 = 9

14 - ... - ... = 9

14 - ... - ... = 9

14 - ... - ... = 9

14 - ... - ... - ... = 9

14 - ... - ... - ... = 9   14 - ... - ... - ... - ... = 9

1. <u>Find</u> the sums. NSS: make ten with bigger number, distribute the smaller number

5		7
9		11
2		4
7		9
4	+ 2	6
10		12
3		5
6		8
1		3
8		10

10		10
6		15
2		11
4		13
9	+ 9	18
5		14
3		12
1		10
7		16
8		17

2		7
10		15
8		13
4		9
3	+ 5	8
7		12
1		6
9		14
6		11
5		10

2. <u>Draw</u> an arrow to connect each number sentence with its matching answer on the number line. The first one is done for you.

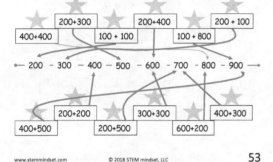

---

1. NSS. <u>Write</u> subtraction number sentences for each picture. <u>Circle</u> the bricks by 5's. <u>Find</u> the value. <u>Draw</u> the black dots for the minuend and then <u>change</u> the black dots into the white dots (or cross out the black dots) to show the subtrahend in the box.

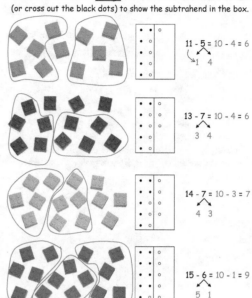

11 - 5 = 10 - 4 = 6
1   4

13 - 7 = 10 - 4 = 6
3   4

14 - 7 = 10 - 3 = 7
4   3

15 - 6 = 10 - 1 = 9
5   1

---

1. <u>Find</u> the sums. NSS: make ten with bigger number, distribute the smaller number.

5		13
9		17
2		10
7		15
4	+ 8	12
10		18
3		11
6		14
1		9
8		16

10		13
6		9
2		5
4		7
9	+ 3	12
5		8
3		6
1		4
7		10
8		11

2		9
10		17
8		15
4		11
3	+ 7	10
7		14
1		8
9		16
6		13
5		12

2. NSS. <u>Write</u> all addition or subtraction number sentences with 1, 2, 3, 4, 5, 6, 7, 8, 9, 10, 11, 12, 13, 14, 15, 16, 17, 18, or 20 so the sum or difference equals 19. You <u>can use</u> each number several times.

1 + 18 = 19   6 + 13 = 19

2 + 17 = 19   7 + 12 = 19

3 + 16 = 19   8 + 11 = 19

4 + 15 = 19   9 + 10 = 19

5 + 14 = 19   20 - 1 = 19

---

1. NSS. <u>Write</u> subtraction number sentences for each picture. <u>Circle</u> the bricks by 5's. <u>Find</u> the value. <u>Draw</u> the black dots for the minuend and then <u>change</u> the black dots into the white dots (or cross out the black dots) to show the subtrahend in the box.

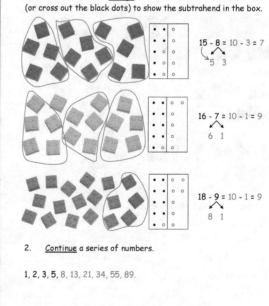

15 - 8 = 10 - 3 = 7
5   3

16 - 7 = 10 - 1 = 9
6   1

18 - 9 = 10 - 1 = 9
8   1

2. <u>Continue</u> a series of numbers.

1, 2, 3, 5, 8, 13, 21, 34, 55, 89.